# Block Periodization

## Breakthrough in Sports Training

By

Vladimir Issurin, Ph.D.

Edited by Dr. Michael Yessis

# Block Periodization
# Breakthrough in Sports Training

By

Vladimir Issurin, Ph.D.

*Elite Sport Department*

at the Wingate Institute for Physical Education and Sport,

Israel

Edited by Dr. Michael Yessis

Published by:

Ultimate Athlete Concepts

Michigan USA

2008

For information and to order copies: www.ultimateathleteconcepts.com

Issurin, Vladimir B.

Block Periodization: Breakthrough in sport training / Vladimir B.Issurin
  p. cm.

Includes bibliographical references.
ISBN  978-0-9817180-0-2

   1.   Physical education and training. 2. High-performance sport.  3. Exercise-Physiological aspects

ISBN  978-0-9817180-0-2

Printed in the United States of America

Ultimate Athlete Concepts
Web site: www.ultimateathleteconcepts.com

**On the cover, clockwise on the top:**
**Chris Carmichael**- world famous coach and his athlete **Lance Armstrong** - world champion in road cycling, 7-Time Tour de France Grand Champion, USA (also page 1)

**Michael Kolganov**- Olympic Bronze Medal Winner, Two-time World Champion in Kayaking, Israel (also page 37)

**Oreste Perri** - Two-time world champion, personal coach of a number of Olympic champions, Head coach of Italian canoe-kayak national team (also page 164)

**Ivan Klementiev**- Olympic champion, seven-time world champion in canoe, member of national parliament of Latvia (also page 128)

**Nicolae Juravschi** (right) and **Victor Renejski** (left) - Two-time Olympic and eight-time World champions, silver Olympic medal winners in canoe, USSR and Republic Moldova

**Gennadi Touretski** (Russia, Switzerland) and his athletes many times Olympic and World champions in swimming **Alexander Popov** (Russia –left) and **Michael Klim** (Australia- right)- (also page 78)

# Contents

# Chapter 2 The workout: general concepts and structure guidelines.37

# Chapter 3 Microcycles, mesocycles and training stages................78

## *Dedication*

To my parents Sofia (Sonia) and Boris Issurin.

May their memory be a blessing for years to come.

# Preface

This book deals with how to improve the training and preparation of athletes to be more successful in high level performances. The bases of contemporary training were founded a few decades ago when the knowledge was far from complete and the level of workloads, results and demands were much lower than now. At that time, traditional *training periodization*, meaning a division of the whole seasonal program into smaller periods and training units, was proposed and explained. This traditional periodization plan was repeated many times and became a universal and monopolistic approach to training planning and analysis.

However, further sports progress showed contradictions between traditional periodization and successful experiences of prominent coaches and athletes. Gradually these experiences led to alternative coaching concepts and, ultimately, to a revamped training approach coined, *Block Periodization*. In general, it assumes the use and sequencing of specialized mesocycle-blocks, in which highly concentrated training workloads are focused on a minimal number of motor and technical abilities. Unlike traditional periodization where simultaneous development of many abilities is prevalent, the block concept proposes consecutive training of carefully selected components. The new approach has been implemented in various sports and has led to outstanding athletic achievements. With this in mind, the purpose of this book is to introduce *Block Periodization* of sports training as a general concept and the basis for a new approach to training.

This book is intended for coaches who perceive their daily pursuit as a creative profession. Coaching as a profession requires a very special combination of knowledge and experience. The author's challenge is to show how knowledge implemented in practice, can form a new positive experience and how by summarizing experiences - new knowledge can be generated.

This book is also for athletes who want to understand why their results do not always meet their expectations. Success in modern sport requires tremendous effort and total dedication. However, the willingness to work harder and harder depends on the athlete's awareness of the aims, means and methods of training. The challenge is to give the athletes a comprehensive explanation of why they must to train hard and how to do it wisely.

In addition, this book is for researchers and other curious people who are looking for new (or relatively new) concepts, approaches and training designs. Sports training deals with the continuous investigation of human nature, and with coaches, at least the more creative among them, who are the true researchers. It is believed that this book will stimulate the curiosity and creativity of such readers.

This book is also for students who still retain doubts about the accessibility of science for training practices. Perhaps after reading this book they will decide that such doubt is superfluous.

There are five chapters in the book that are united by the general idea of Block Periodization that provides both the scientific background and practical consequences of this revamped training system. Chapter 1 elucidates the Block Periodization concept. This chapter presents criticism of traditional periodization and provides the bases and benefits of the alternative approach. Chapter 2 deals with the single workout, namely, workout types and structures, sequence and compatibility of different exercises, and the structure of a one day training series. Chapter 3 explains how to design different type training microcycles. Also, the mesocycles for accumulation, transmutation and realization are analyzed and discussed. Chapter 4 is devoted to long-term preparation, namely, to annual and quadrennial plans, and the bases of long-term preparation of adult and junior athletes. The basic approach to identifying gifted youngsters is given special consideration. Chapter 5 describes the bases of altitude training, focused in particular on how to construct the optimal Block Periodization plan that includes training camps at altitude. The proposed guidelines are based on long-term experiences of high-level athletes in altitude training.

In summary, during the last decades the achievements of athletes and their sports mastery have improved tremendously. The main factor for this breakthrough, which is obvious to all professional observers, is the progress in the preparation of athletes. This has been noted in many professional reports, anecdotal statements and in various publications, mostly journals and coaching magazines. However, current training textbooks and coaching guidelines are still far from complete and a large body of training knowledge is available only to a small group of experts. This book is unique that it links successful experiences in sport practice with the scientific bases of sports training. It consolidates both of the empirically proven positions with up-to-date knowledge. The author hopes that the book will meet the expectations of readers who perceive sports training as an area of creativity, self-confirmation and human progress.

# Acknowledgements

The book summarizes the findings of many studies conducted in cooperation with my colleagues and friends. The first papers on Block Periodization were published with Dr. Vassily Kaverin (Moscow) who at that time served as head-coach of the USSR canoe-kayak team. A number of publications were written with Gilad Lustig, Vladimir Shkliar, Leonid Kaufman from Israel; and Prof. Gershon Tenenbaum from Florida State University (USA). Their willing cooperation is very much appreciated.

The book contains practical examples supplied by my colleagues and friends: Dr. Boris Blumenshtein, Gennadi Hiskia, Mark Tunis, Omrit Yanilov-Eden (all from Israel), and Prof. Anatoly Bondarchuk from Canada. Very valuable information was provided by the great swimming coach Gennadi Touretski, representing Russia and Switzerland. I am extremely grateful to each of them for their contribution.

A number of world famous coaches and athletes reviewed several parts of this book and/or cooperated with me in different stages of my life. They are the coaches of world and Olympic champions including Chris Carmichael (USA), Oreste Perri (Italy), Gennadi Touretski (Russia, Switzerland), and great athletes who earned gold medals in world championships and Olympic Games, Nikolae Juravschi (Moldova), Ivan Klementiev (Latvia), Michael Kolganov (Israel), and Alexander Popov (Russia). Special thanks to these great professionals and amazing personalities for sharing their experiences and knowledge with me for this book.

I discussed and deliberated over several scientific positions with the late Prof. Atko Viru (Estonia), whose valuable comments cannot be underestimated.
I thank also Mr. Mike Garmise for his valuable assistance in editing the initial text.

I would also like to thank Dr. Michael Yessis for his invaluable expertise in doing the final edit of this book. His highly professional efforts greatly assisted to make this book more easily understood in English.

Last but certainly not least, the person who has had the strongest influence on my work and life, Prof. Vladimir Zatsiorsky (Penn State University, USA). I am extremely grateful for his valuable comments on an earlier version of this book, for his readiness to help and for his life-long friendship.

Finally, I want to thank my wife Irena. While she did not take part in any of the studies reported in this book, she affected all my efforts as I worked on the manuscript. Ultimately these efforts resulted in this book.

# Chapter 1

Chris Carmichael- world famous coach and his athlete

Lance Armstrong - world champion in road cycling, 7-Time Tour de France Grand

Champion, USA

# Chapter 1

# Block periodization
# vs. traditional theory

Many generations of scientists, coaches and athletes have tried to build a training system that would yield the best performance results. Their efforts have focused on three general problems:

- How to design an effective training plan for a sufficiently long period.
- How to optimally implement such a plan.
- How to achieve the most favorable combination of all athletic abilities exactly at the time of the main competition.

These problems belong to *training periodization*, the purposeful sequencing of different training units (long, medium and short-term training cycles and sessions) so that the athlete can attain the desired state and planned for results. Because training periodization contains many variables and depends on many circumstances, the ideal model can exist only in theory. Nevertheless, each year we take another step towards more conscious planning and a more complete understanding of training as a whole.

This chapter summarizes the two most prevalent views of training periodization, (a) the traditional approach which has been dominant for a long time, and (b) block periodization, which has come into widespread use among high-level athletes during the last decades.

## 1.1. Traditional theory of periodization, basics and limitations

Training periodization was founded during the 1950s in the former USSR and was established as a scientific concept by Matveyev in 1964. This theory spread to Eastern Europe (Ozolin,1970; Harre,1973) and later to Western countries (Dick, 1980; Martin, 1980; Bompa, 1984; Yessis, 1987), and constituted a compulsory part of training in high-performance sport. In general, periodization exploits the periodic changes in human biological and social activities. For a long time, this theory was accepted as the universal basis for training in any sport and for athletes on any level of competency.

The first criticisms and calls for reform appeared in the early 1980s in elite sport as the experience of top coaches stood in contrast to the entrenched theories. New approaches proposed by creative coaches and scientists appeared. Extensive discussions by sports experts took place in the 1990s in East and West European sports magazines. Let us first examine the basics of traditional theory and their limitations from the viewpoint of high-performance sport.

### 1.1.1. The scope of traditional theory

The cornerstones of periodization are formed by a hierarchical system of training units that are periodically repeated (Table 1.1). The upper level of the hierarchy belongs to the Olympic quadrennial cycle, juxtaposed with other great events in the sports world. The next level of the hierarchy is represented by the macrocycles. A macrocycle usually lasts one year but can be shortened to half a year and even less. This flexibility in the annual cycle subdivision is irrelevant to the block periodization approach. The macrocycles are divided into training periods. The training periods fulfill a key function in traditional theory because they divide the macrocycle into two major parts: the first for more generalized and preliminary work (preparatory period); (the second for more event-specific work in the specialized pre competitive period) and competition (competitive period).

In addition, a third but short period is set aside for active recovery and rehabilitation. The next two levels of the hierarchy are reserved for the mesocycles (medium-size training cycles) and microcycles (small-size training cycles). The bottom of the hierarchy belongs to workouts and exercises, which are the building elements of the entire training system.

**Table 1.1**

**Hierarchy and duration of the training periods**

| Training periods | Time duration | Mode of planning |
|---|---|---|
| Quadrennial (Olympic) cycle | Four years – period between Olympic Games | Long-term |
| Macrocycle, perhaps annual cycle | One year or several months | |
| Mesocycle | Several weeks | Medium-term |
| Microcycle | One week or several days | |
| Workout or training session | Several hours (usually not more than three) | Short-term |
| Training exercise | Minutes (usually) | |

The training periods provide sufficient freedom in the training design. External factors, such as the competition calendar and seasonal changes, dictate peaking phases and restrictions in training. As a result, a coach can select the sequencing, content and duration of the training cycles and define the specifics of the means and methods for each training.

The traditional approach points out the general characteristics of the above-mentioned periods and subdivides them into several stages. The training content of each stage is very definite with regard to workload volume and intensity (Table 1.2).

**Table 1.2**

**General characteristics of training periodization in the traditional approach**

**(based on Matveyev, 1981)**

| Period | Stage | Aims | Workload |
|---|---|---|---|
| Preparatory | General preparatory | Raising the level of general motor abilities. Increasing the repertory of various motor skills. | Relatively great volume and reduced intensity of the main exercises, great variety of training means |
| | Special preparatory | Development of a specific training level, development of more specialized motor and technical abilities | Load volume reaches maximum and intensity increases selectively |
| Competitive | Competitive preparation | Enhancing event-specific motor abilities, technical and tactical skills and forming individual patterns of competitive performance | Stabilization and reduction of volume together with an increase of intensity in event-specific exercises |
| | Immediate pre-competitive training | Achieving event-specific fitness and attaining readiness for the main competition | Low volume, high intensity, full modeling of forthcoming competition |
| Transitional | Transitory | Recovery | Active rest with the use of various pleasant activities |

Initially the traditional approach assumes one macrocycle a year; a typical design is presented in Figure 1.1.

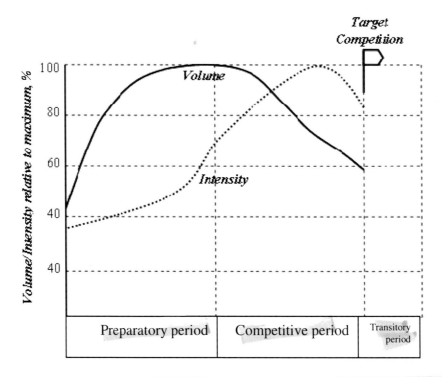

**Figure 1.1.** Traditional presentation of annual cycle with one macrocycle (one-peak annual periodization)

The one-peak annual cycle was particularly suitable for seasonal sports such as skiing, skating, rowing etc. but did not meet the sports demands when athletes competed in any and all seasons (fencing, swimming, some dual and team sports). Later modifications had two and three macrocycles within the annual cycle. Each macrocyle was subdivided into three periods characterized by specific combinations of training objectives and workloads (Figure 1.2).

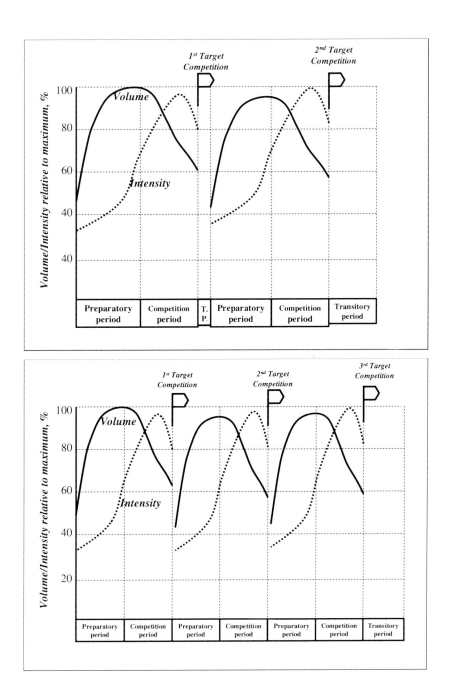

**Figure 1.2.** Annual cycle with two- and three macrocycles (two- and three-peak annual periodization)

The mesocycles, the medium sized training cycles, have been interpreted in different ways. The Block Periodization Concept uses a more simplified mesocycle classification.

The microcycles, as the shortest training cycles, have fewer contradictions. Despite the lack of unanimity among authors in regard to the names of the different microcycles, the following summary may help clarify the situation (Table 1.3.)

## Table 1.3
## Microcycle types based on a summary of many publications

| Name* | General characteristics |
|---|---|
| Adjustment, involving, initializing | Medium load level, gradual increase in workload |
| Loading, developmental, ordinary | Increased load level, use of big and substantial workloads |
| Impact, shock, extreme loads | Use of and summation of extreme workloads |
| Pre-competitive, tuning, peaking | Medium load level, the use of event-specific means and methods. |
| Competitive | Sport and event-specific performance |
| Restoration, regeneration | Low load level, use of a wide spectrum of restorative means |

* The underlined title is the version preferred by the author

### 1.1.2. Positives and Negatives of the traditional approach

The traditional theory of training athletes was formulated at a time when there was limited knowledge and little scientifically proven guidelines for coaching. Traditional training periodization, which adopted the up-to-date know-how of the 1960s, was a breakthrough for coaching and training science. Many of the elements postulated then remain valid to this day, including the hierarchical taxonomy and terminology of training cycles, the differentiation between general and specialized athletic preparation, changes in exercise volume and intensity, basic approaches to short-term, medium-term and long-term planning, etc. It would be unrealistic to expect that all of the ideas proposed more than four decades ago would remain applicable today. Thus, several of the principles of athletic preparation are not important in the alternative Training Block approach.

> **Example**. The *principle of unity of general and specialized preparation*
> was postulated in the traditional theory in regard to high level performance.
> Training downplayed the importance of event-specific means during long periods
> of general preparation, where this specificity could be ignored. Conversely, the
> importance of general exercises could be ignored during long competitive periods,
> when specific means are predominant.
>
> The *principle of continuity* was relevant when athletes lost motivation to
> train during long periods of monotonous training long before serious competition.
> The principle of *wave-shape training* was important to prevent overloading so
> prevalent during prolonged periods of hard workloads typical of traditional
> planning.

The traditional design is still appropriate for low-level athletes. It does not
work well for high-performance athletes. Traditional theory also contains a number of
contradictions which dramatically reduce preparation effectiveness. (See table 1.4).

For instance, preparatory period training for high level athletes in endurance
sports, martial arts, dual and team sports and aesthetic sports, assumes the
development of general aerobic abilities, muscle strength and strength endurance,
improvement in general coordination and explosive ability, basic mental and technical
preparation, mastery of the tactical repertoire, and treatment of previous injuries. Each
of these factors requires specific physiological, morphological and psychological
adaptation. However many of the workloads are not compatible and create
conflicting responses.

**Table 1.4**

**The main contradictions of the traditional training approach for high-level athletes (Issurin, 2007)**

| Factors | Contradictions | Consequences |
|---|---|---|
| Energy supply | There is sufficient energy supply for concurrent performance of diversified workloads | Energy is directed to many targets while the main target doesn't get the appropriate attention. |
| Restoration of different physiological systems | Because of differing periods for recuperation of different physiological systems, athletes do not get sufficient restoration | Athletes become fatigued and can't concentrate their full effort on the main objectives |
| Compatibility of various workloads | Different exercises often interact negatively due to energy deficits, technical complexity and/or neuromuscular fatigue | Executing certain loads eliminates or reduces the effect of previous or subsequent workouts |
| Mental concentration | Doing stressful workloads demand high levels of mental concentration that can't be directed at many targets simultaneously | Mental concentration dissipates and exercises are performed with reduced attention and motivation |
| Training stimulus for progress | Sport-specific progress of high-level athletes demands large amounts of training stimuli that can't be obtained by concurrently training for many factors | Complex simultaneous development of many abilities doesn't provide sufficient improvement for high-level athletes |

**Study and example.** Highly qualified male swimmers were studied during eight weeks of early season preparation. The athletes performed a strenuous fitness program combined with extensive swimming, which included resistive exercises and power drills directed to the development of swimming-specific strength. The total number of workouts was usually 9-11 per week The training outcomes were evaluated, maximal force of tethered swimming ($F_{tsw}$), dry-land explosive strength ($F_{exp}$), and dry-land strength endurance ($SE$). The fitness program resulted in remarkable improvement in strength endurance, while the swim-specific strength and explosive strength didn't improve (Figure 1.3). During this entire period the swimmers improved their swimming preparedness, evaluated mostly by endurance tests.

Therefore, the global aim of the fitness program was not obtained. Although the swimmers enhanced their strength endurance, they did not improve their maximum swim-specific strength, and their explosive strength decreased. Despite a substantial part of the program devoted to maximal and explosive strength exercises (about 30% of the time expended in a dry-land program), the expected training effect was dramatically impaired by the negative interaction of the workloads with the strength endurance routines and extensive swimming program.

A maximum strength program requires muscles hypertrophy and enhancement of the neural mechanism of muscular contraction. The latter is of primary importance for improving explosive strength. The extensive endurance workloads capture the metabolic energy that is necessary for anabolism during post-exercise recovery. This suppresses muscle hypertrophy.

Enhancement of the neural mechanism is conditioned by the state of the central nervous system and the sensitivity of the neuro-motor pool (Klausen, 1990). The observations of coaches and athletes show that a strenuous high volume training program causes permanent fatigue. As a result, the central and peripheral neural factors are far from optimum, which is needed for improvement of the muscular contraction.

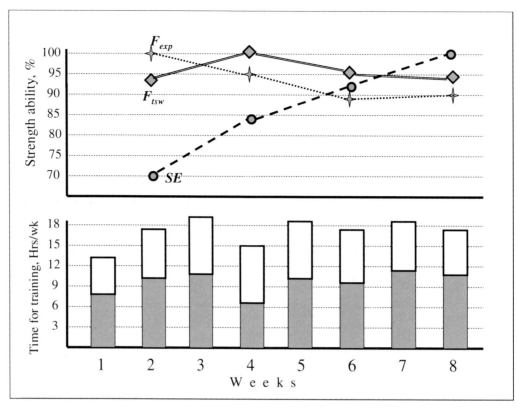

**Figure 1.3** Key: Maximum force of tethered swimming ($F_{tsw}$), explosive strength ($F_{exp}$) measured as the force achieved during 0.2 s of isometric effort in stroke simulation, and strength endurance ($SE$) measured as the power output during two minutes of two-arm stroke simulation on an isokinetic machine by high-level swimmers during an eight-week fitness program. Bottom half – training time expended for fitness (white boxes) and time for swimming routines (grey boxes)

Similar situations were experienced by many coaches, but not all of them were critically assessed. The most prominent coaches decided that developmental programs for maximum and explosive strength and strength endurance should be separate. They found that the problem with high-level athletes is that their progress demands large highly-concentrated workloads, that can not be simultaneously managed to achieve many different objectives.

An additional drawback of the traditional scheme is its inability to prepare athletes for successful participation in many competitions. Even the three-peak annual cycle design does not satisfy the international sport trend towards competitions throughout the year. The multi-peak tendency that is in obvious contradiction with traditional planning, is very characteristic of modern high-level sport. Let's consider the above-mentioned multi-peak tendency in the example of the world-class track and field athletes.

---

**Example**. Data on three world class athletes, Marion Jones (USA), Sergei Bubka (Soviet Union, Ukraine since 1991), and Stefka Kostadinova (Bulgaria) show that each had pre-season and in-season preparation lasting about 300-320 days (Table 1.5). As can be seen in the table, the time span when these athletes competed and reached peak-achievements, and when they had relatively low results varied between 135 – 265 days. This long time span can not be subdivided into traditional preparatory and competitive periods.

On the other hand, the basic abilities of these athletes (maximum strength, capacity of aerobic regeneration) should be maintained on a sufficiently high level during the 5 to 8 month span. Therefore, the appropriate training cycles for basic abilities and recovery should be incorporated into the program. The traditional scheme doesn't resolve this problem and is unable to provide such preparation in the basic plan.

---

**Table 1.5**

**Multi-peak annual preparation of world-class track and field athletes**

**(based on Suslov, 2001; with modifications)**

| Athlete, event, best achievements | Year | Number of peaks in season | Typical intervals between the peaks | Total time span for competing |
|---|---|---|---|---|
| Marion Jones; 100-200m, long jump, 3-time Olympic Champion in 2000, 5-time World Champion | 1998 | 10* | 19-22 days | 200 days |
| Sergei Bubka; pole vault, Olympic Champion 1988, 5-time World Champion world record holder | 1991 | 7** | 23-43 days | 265 days |
| Stefka Kostadinova; high jump, Olympic Champion 1996, 2-time World Champion, world record holder | 1998 | 11*** | 14-25 days | Winter -20 days; spring and summer – 135 days |

* There were eight peaks in running and two separate peaks in the long jump; all the peaks were on the level of her personal, best results;

** All the peaks were within 3% of his personal best result, namely –595-612 cm;

*** All the peaks were within 3% of her personal best result, namely –200-205 cm

The above noted disadvantage of traditional planning was recognized by many coaches. They modified the annual chart and inserted relatively short-term training cycles with highly concentrated workloads to ensure multi-peak preparation. These were, in fact, the precursors of alternative training periodization. A few decades ago high-level coaches could be heard lamenting, "We build up massive foundations of basic abilities, but when we complete at the tower of specific fitness (peak), the foundations are mired in a bog." This gloomy outlook reflected the practical observation that prolonged development of basic abilities doesn't guarantee the maintenance of these abilities at the achieved high level. Unfavorable in-season changes in physiological and sport-specific variables were noted and commented upon in many follow-up studies dealing with the preparation of high-level athletes. The pattern of these typical changes is presented in Figure 1.4.

**Study and example.** A group of highly qualified kayakers was studied during their yearly preparation designed on the classical model. The incremental pattern step test was used to determine velocity at anaerobic threshold ((V-AT) and mean distance velocity in all-out performance (Vd). Peak Force on the paddle (PF) and Stroke Rate (SR) were obtained with the help of a portable telemetry system. Anthropometric measurements made it possible to calculate muscle mass (MM). As can be seen in Fig.1.3, the long period of general preparation (preparatory period) caused a substantial increase in aerobic endurance (V-AT), muscle mass and strength (peak force on the paddle).

During the relatively long period of highly specialized competition, extensive aerobic workloads were replaced by more intense event-specific exercises. Maximum strength exercises were reduced and even rejected as harmful for racing technique. As a result, the velocity at anaerobic threshold and peak force decreased during the competitive period, and muscle mass diminished prior to competition. It is worth noting that mean distance velocity reached maximum for the main competition, obtained by the increased stroke rate despite reduced force application to the paddle. It is obvious that the timing pattern for developing different abilities was far from optimal (Issurin et al., 1986).

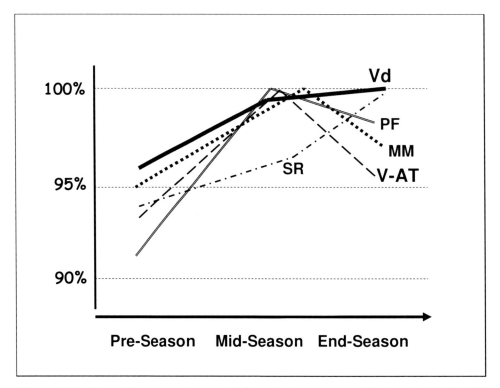

**Figure 1.4.** Mean distance velocity (Vd), velocity at anaerobic threshold (V-AT), peak force on the paddle (PF), stroke rate (SR) and muscle mass (MM) of high-level kayakers during one annual macrocycle (based on Issurin et al.,1986).

### 1.1.3. Why traditional planning should be revised

As can be inferred from above, the drawbacks to the traditional training concept were a crucial factor in seeking an alternative approach. These limitations included:

- restrictions created by the simultaneous development of a number of motor and technical abilities;
- the inability to provide multi-peak preparation, i.e. successful participation in many competitions;
- excessively long periods of basic and sport-specific preparation.

Moreover, the tremendous changes in world sport in recent decades are having a strong influence on the evolution of the training process. While the variety and uniqueness of each sport makes it difficult to be specific, these changes can be summarized as follows:

*Key for FB, even though they are close together*

16

- a dramatic increase in the number of competitions and competitive performances;
- a remarkable reduction in the total volume of training workloads;
- the appearance of new concepts affecting the planning and designing of alternative training periodization.

**Increase in the number of competitions**

In contemporary sport, participation in competition throughout the entire season and a remarkable increase in the number of competitive days throughout the year can be seen (Figure 1.5).

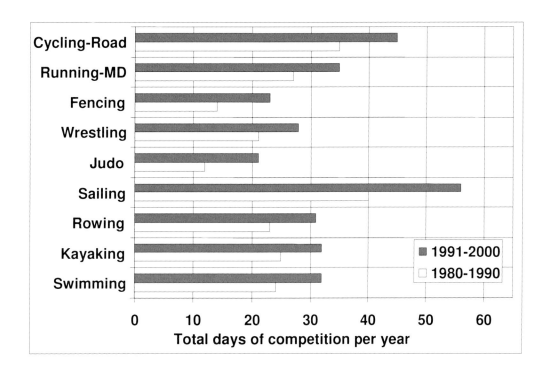

**Figure 1.5.** The number of competitive days for international class athletes in different sports. Data obtained from internationally recognized experts in the sports mentioned (Issurin, 2007).

At least three factors have determined the trend in competitive activity. They are:

1. **An increase in the number of competitions** in the last two decades in international and national schedules. International sports federations have initiated and supported the organization of the traditional series of grand prix, world and continental cups, memorial trophies etc., which have become popular among top athletes and the sports media. Also, national federations have built extensive competition schedules intended to engage a larger population of sub-elite athletes in ambitious preparatory programs;

2. **The financial motivation of top athletes** has increased substantially. The premiums prize-winners can receive have become strong stimuli to reach peak-performance levels more frequently than proposed in the traditional periodization scheme. At the same time, second echelon athletes have modified their competitive strategy to imitate the top athletes' patterns;

3. **The contribution of competition** to training has increased dramatically. More frequent competition breaks the training routine and changes the relationship between loading and recovery. Advanced coaches exploite more frequent competition to intensify the athlete's preparation.

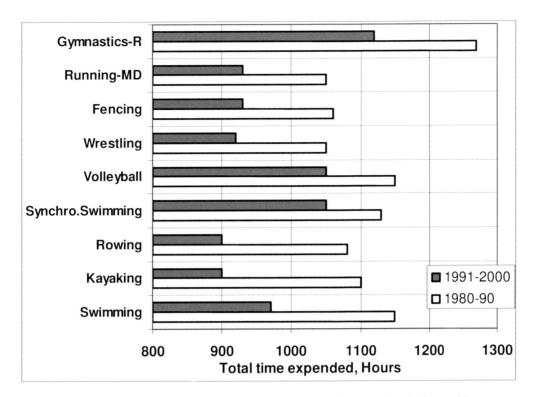

**Figure 1.6.** Total training time in one year among international class athletes (data obtained from internationally recognized experts in the sports mentioned); Gymnastics-R – Rhythmic Gymnastics, Running-MD – Running middle distance (Issurin, 2007).

4. **Reduction in total volume of training workloads** among high-performance athletes. Figure 1.6 illustrates this in different sports from various countries. A number of circumstances can be cited for this global trend. They are:

   a. Remarkable progress in training methods and sports technologies. Up-to-date knowledge of long-, medium-, and short-term training effects makes it possible to design training programs that prevent excessive workloads, which were often the result of insufficient understanding or critical appraisal. Monitoring technologies for heart rate, blood lactate, movement rate and technique have been incorporated into training routines so that acute and immediate training effects are now much more measurable and predictable. The modern approach to planning training has made it possible to replace the slogan, "more miles make champions" to "knowledge gives power". This factor closely interacts with the next one.

b. Worldwide sharing of successful experiences among coaches. It is obvious that the modern world of elite-sport has become more open and dynamic. International training centers host athletes from different countries for training camps and extended preparation. Coaches' clinics, seminars and courses engage experts of world renown, who don't hesitate to lay out – for all to see and hear – items that were once classified as "top secret". Many successful coaches from countries that regulated experience-sharing by means of strictly enforced sport policies have taken the world as their stage. These are coaches possessing long-term experience in the use of extreme and standard training workloads, from the time when general training volumes were strictly prescribed. They knew that a substantial part of these excessive workloads were not useful, if not harmful, and now they share this knowledge with colleagues from many countries.

c. Increases in the number of competitions and starts. The excessive training loads were partly superseded by more pronounced competitive activity.

d. Rejection of illegal pharmacological products. It is no secret that use of some illegal pharmacologicals facilitated certain athletes' physiological responses, such as muscular hypertrophy and speed of recovery, and affected higher workload performance. Doping control -- before, during and after competitions – initiated by the International Olympic Committee in the mid 1990s has become an indispensable part of modern sport and has helped prevent the use and sharing of these harmful technologies in high-performance sport. The end result was a reduction in the athletes ability to maintain high-load training programs.

e. Social and political changes in post-communist countries. It is common knowledge that the highest workload volumes were performed by athletes of former communist countries where athletic preparation was strictly centralized. Integrative parameters of the training process (such as total mileage, total time expended on training, etc.) were imposed on national teams in the form of planning directives. Very often these directives proposed excessive training workloads as a tool to attain more successful athletic performances.

The social and political changes that these countries underwent were followed by the democratization of elite-sport, a reduction in administrative pressure and liberation of the coaches. This allowed them to display individual initiative. On the other hand, the economical upheavals brought about by the political changes in these countries exhausted most of the financial resources available to high-level sport. As a consequence, total workload volumes were substantially reduced. In a ripple effect, this change influenced training volume trends in other countries and caused load reductions there as well.

All of these circumstances and factors contributed to the search for alternative training approaches by creative coaches and scientists having a practical orientation. Not every attempt to reform the traditional system was successful. However, revisions gradually became bolder and more desirable for preparing high-level athletes in the new era of more competitions. In addition, a highly developed sports industry and a more open sports society demanded a revamping of the training system. As a result, several new concepts were implemented and created the foundation for alternative periodization and advanced training theory.

## 1.2. The Block Periodization Concept - general outline

### 1.2.1. New concepts affecting the rationalize and design of alternative training periodization.

In the 1980s, the concept that emerged from prominent coaches pertained to what was called, *training blocks*. This idea was not conceptualized scientifically and was open to different interpretations. However, in its most comprehensive meaning, *training block* referred to a training cycle of highly concentrated specialized workloads. This definition corresponds to the common understanding of *the block* as an autonomous compact unit of several elements combined for a specific function. Further consideration of training blocks as a coaching concept led to several logical consequences:

- Highly concentrated training workloads for many qualities cannot be managed at the same time. Therefore, the training block is an alternative to the widespread practice of simultaneous complex development of many abilities;
- Athletic performance in any sport usually demands the mastery of many abilities, which, in the case of training blocks, can only be developed consecutively, not concurrently;
- Developing a process that includes morphological, organic and biochemical changes requires a sufficiently long time period of about 2-6 weeks, which corresponds to the duration of mesocycles. Hence, training blocks are mostly *mesocycle-blocks.*

One of the most successful coaches to achieve great results using this alternative training system was Anatoly Bondarchuk, who coached the gold-, silver-, and bronze-medal winners in the hammer throw at the 1988 and other Olympic Games. He fulfilled the nearly unattainable dream of having the entire Olympic podium occupied by athletes of the same coach. Based on his own personal athletic experience (he was Olympic hammer throw champion in 1972) and careful investigation of throwers' training programs (as part of his doctoral studies in 1988), Bondarchuk created the original periodization chart that completely reformed the traditional approaches to training (Bondarchuk, 1986 and 1988).

Dr. Bondarchuk established three types of specialized mesocycle-blocks: **developmental**, where workload levels gradually increase to maximum; **competitive**, where the load level is stabilized and athletes focus on the competitive performance; and **restorative**, where athletes utilize active recovery and prepare for the next developmental program. The duration of the two first types of mesocycles is usually four weeks while the third can be shortened to two weeks. The sequencing of these blocks depends on the competition schedule and on the responses of individual athletes. The outstanding characteristic of this training program design is alternation and repetition of the exercise repertory in each mesocycle-block (every four weeks). The terms of traditional periodization like "preparatory, competitive and transitory periods" were used, but the author noted that in his concept their essence is very different.

As already mentioned, the "winds of reformation" became stronger in the earlier 1980s. At that time elite USSR canoe-kayak paddlers performed an enormous exercise volume. The prevailing opinion was that this load level was excessive and that the training design could be made more effective. The idea of training blocks and mesocycle- sequencing was conceptualized, implemented and proved in practice, and then published (Issurin & Kaverin, 1985). Three types of mesocycle-blocks were elucidated: **accumulation**, which was devoted to developing basic abilities such as general aerobic endurance, muscle strength, and general patterns of movement technique; **transformation**, which focused on developing specific abilities like combined aerobic-anaerobic or anaerobic endurance, specialized muscle endurance, and event-specific technique; and **realization**, which was designed as a pre-competitive training phase that focused mainly on race model exercises, attaining maximum speed and recovery prior to the forthcoming competition.

*[handwritten margin note: ✳ Accumulation 4 wks / Transformation 4 wks / Realization 2 wks.]*

The duration of the mesocycles was established according to physiological and biochemical prerequisites that usually allowed four weeks for the accumulation and transformation mesocycles, and two weeks for realization. These three mesocycles were combined into a separate training stage which ended with competition. A number of training stages formed the annual macrocycle, which was formally subdivided into preparatory and competitive periods, but this differentiation was of minor importance.

The modified training design allowed for about a 10-15% reduction in the annual training volume. Follow-up testing of the national team during preparation showed considerable improvement in the main fitness components in all subgroups. The radically reformed preparation program resulted in outstanding performances in the 1988 Seoul Olympic Games (three gold and three silver medals) and in the 1989 and 1990 World Championships where eight and nine gold medals, respectively, were won.

Another concept affecting the clarification and implementation of the alternative preparation approach is the residual training effect (see glossary), a term first coined by Brian and James Counsilman (1991). Compared to other types of training effects (acute, immediate, cumulative and delayed), residual effect remains relatively new and obscure. The residual training effect refers to *the retention of*

*changes induced by systematic workloads beyond a certain time period after the*
*cessation of training.*

The residual training effect phenomenon is closely connected with detraining, which was previously understood as a loss of "trainedness" when training was stopped. In fact, detraining in high-performance sport usually occurs selectively, according to specific abilities when not stimulated by sufficient training. For instance, maximum oxygen uptake among highly trained endurance athletes decreases when total weekly volume is reduced below a certain level (Steinacker, 1993; Steinacker et al., 1998). Similarly, large volumes of highly intense exercises do not prevent detraining and loss of aerobic endurance during the taper (Mujika, 1999).

When training is designed in the traditional manner and many abilities are developed simultaneously, the risk of detraining is negligible because each quality (motor or technical ability) receives some portion of the training stimuli. However, if these abilities are developed consecutively, as proposed above (Issurin & Kaverin, 1985, Bondarchuk, 1986, 1988), the problem of detraining becomes very important. If you develop one ability and lose another one at the same time, you have to take into account the duration of the positive effect of the given training after its cessation and how fast you will lose the obtained ability level when you stop training it. In other words, you have to know the residual effect of each type of training. A recent study presents data summarizing the duration of the training residuals with regard to different motor abilities (Table 1.6.)

**Table 1.6**

**The duration and physiological background of the residual training effects for different motor abilities after cessation of training (Issurin & Lustig, 2004)**

| Motor ability | Residual duration, days | Physiological background |
|---|---|---|
| Aerobic endurance | 30 ± 5 | Increased amount of aerobic enzymes, number of mitochondria, muscle capillaries, hemoglobin capacity, glycogen storage and higher rate of fat metabolism |
| Maximum strength | 30 ± 5 | Improvement of neural mechanism and muscle hypertrophy due mainly to muscle fiber enlargement |
| Anaerobic glycolitic endurance | 18 ± 4 | Increased amount of anaerobic enzymes, buffering capacity and glycogen storage and higher possibility of lactate accumulation |
| Strength endurance | 15 ± 5 | Muscle hypertrophy mainly in slow-twitch fibers, improved aerobic/anaerobic enzymes, better local blood circulation and lactic acid tolerance |
| Maximum speed (alactic) | 5 ± 3 | Improved neuro-muscular interactions and motor control, increased phosphocreatine storage |

*↳ How long could CNS last to not lose Max Speed adaptation?? If you wanted speed often...*

The rate of loss of the training effects and respective training residuals vary widely for different motor abilities. Some physiological systems retain increased levels of adaptation longer than others. For example, improved aerobic capacity is determined by pronounced morphological and biochemical changes, i.e., increases in capillary density, glycogen storage and in particular, the amount of aerobic enzymes, which increase by 40-90% (Volkov,1986; Fox et al.,1993; Wilmore & Costill, 1993). This is in contrast to the much lesser local adaptations seen in athletes after sprint training such as increases in phosphocreatine storage (2-5%), peak lactate accumulation (10-20%) and anaerobic enzymes (2-20 %). Consequently, aerobic ability, which is supported by pronounced morphological and biochemical changes, is retained for a number of weeks at near-peak level, while anaerobic abilities,

*→Morphological: Shape changes*

particularly maximum sprint speed, retain near-peak levels for much shorter periods (Table 1.6).

Maximum strength gains in top-level athletes are determined by pronounced morphological, biochemical and neural changes, such as enlargement of the cross-sectional area of muscle fibers, increased number of fibers (hyperplasia), recruitment of previously inactive motor units and synchronization of their activity, and increased discharge frequency of motor-neurons (Zatsiorsky, 1995). All these significant adaptations create a relatively long training residual for strength training.

Training residuals of strength endurance are dependent on the duration of the event and the degree of mobilization of anaerobic resources. Strength endurance for long-duration performance has relatively longer residuals, thanks to pronounced aerobic adaptation.

The changes induced by training for peak speed are characterized by fewer gains and shorter residuals. Highly concentrated sprint training causes relatively small increases in quickly available energy sources such as ATP and phosphocreatine, and enzymes such as creatine kinase (Thorstensson, 1988). In addition, peak speed is based on very delicate and highly precise neuro-muscular interactions, which are relatively unstable and cannot be maintained at the highest level without specially organized training.

This knowledge about training residuals and the time of detraining is important when the planning turns from simultaneous to consecutive development of sport-specific fitness components. When we stop developing a specific ability we should be able to predict how long this ability will remain at the "sufficient" level. This information should determine the appropriate sequencing and timing of the training cycles.

## 1.2.2. General principles of the Block Periodization Concept

The revised approach, called the Block Periodization Concept (BPC) has been developed and finalized with general principles and with guidelines for the training systems.

**The general principles** of this training system are displayed in Figure 1.7.

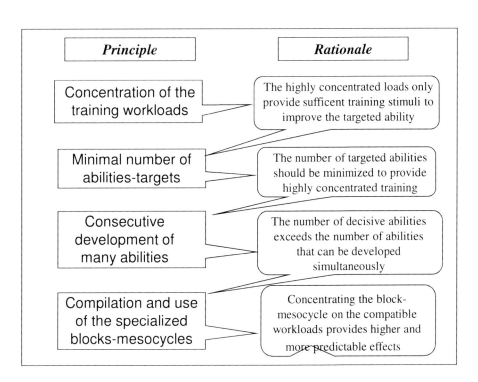

**Figure 1.7.** General principles of the Block Periodization Concept and the rationale for determining their unity and subordination (Issurin, 2007).

Concentration of training workloads is the most decisive and fundamental principle of the BPC. The rationale behind it is the long-known fact that only highly concentrated training workloads can produce a sufficient stimulus in high-level athletes for greater gains in a given motor and/or technical ability. This is the cornerstone from which the following principles emerge:

1.  Highly concentrated training demands a minimum number of abilities that can be affected simultaneously (the alternative is a complex design where many abilities are developed simultaneously);

2.  Consecutive development is the only possible approach when the number of sport-specific abilities needed is more than the number of abilities that can be trained simultaneously (the alternative complex approach has no hard limitation in regard to this factor, where one mesocycle and microcycle combine the workloads for many abilities); and

3.  The mesocycle-blocks should be specialized and structured to produce one of three different effects: *accumulation* (athletes accumulate the basic

27

motor and technical abilities); *transmutation* (athletes transmute their motor potential to event-specific preparedness); and *realization* (athletes realize their preparedness as readiness for competition and attain the planned result).

Therefore, the medium size training cycles, called mesocycle-blocks, are the most prominent embodiment of the Block Periodization Concept. They are much more concentrated, more specialized, and more manageable in the training programs.

### 1.2.3. Structuring the annual cycle

As in the traditional approach, annual cycle planning begins by determining the target competitions scheduled by international and national sport authorities. The training program becomes apparent in the subdivision of the annual cycle into a number of training stages, each of which contains three types of mesocycles: accumulation, transmutation and realization (Table 1.7).

**Table 1.7**

**The main characteristics of the three types of mesocycle-blocks (Issurin, 2007)**

*[handwritten: Transmutation + Transformation are synonamous.]*

| Main characteristics | Type of Mesocycle | | |
|---|---|---|---|
| | **Accumulation** | **Transmutation** | **Realization** |
| Targets specific motor and technical abilities | Basic abilities; aerobic endurance, muscular strength, basic coordination | Sport-specific abilities; special endurance, strength endurance, proper technique | Integrative preparedness; model performances, maximum speed, event specific tactics |
| Volume-intensity | High volume, reduced intensity | Reduced volume, increased intensity | Low-medium volume, high intensity |
| Fatigue-restoration | Reasonable restoration to provide morphological adaptation | Not possibile to provide full restoration, fatigue accumulated | Full restoration, athletes should be well rested |
| Follow-up | Monitoring the level of basic abilities | Monitoring the level of sport-specific abilities | Monitoring maximum speed, event specific strategy etc. |

The rational sequencing of the mesocycles within each training stage makes it possible to carry over optimal residual training effects as shown in Figure 1.8. It shows how it is possible to have interaction of training residuals to provide high level competitive performance with the optimal amounts of all motor and technical abilities. This is based on the fact that training residuals of basic abilities last much longer than residuals of more specific abilities, with residuals of maximal speed and event-specific readiness the shortest (Table 1.6).

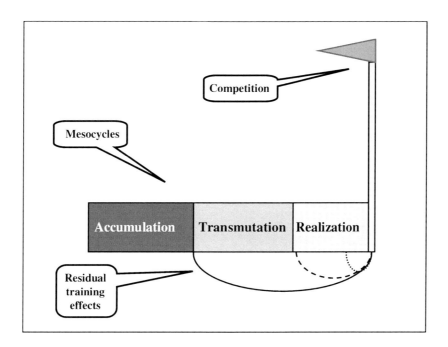

**Figure 1.8.** Superimposing of residual training effects induced by sequenced mesocycle-blocks (Issurin & Shkliar, 2002).

In figure 1.8, the duration of the training stage is determined by the duration of the training residuals and should be about two months. In actual fact, the training stages can be shorter as for example, when close to season peaking, or longer, when at the beginning of the season to meet specific needs. In the second case (longer training stages), special measures should be used to prolong residual training effects (see short-term planning). It is worth noting that each training stage gives the appearance of an annual cycle in miniature. It includes a training block resembling the preparation period (accumulation), a training block resembling the competition period (transmutation), and ends with tapering (realization) and competitive performance.

Based on the above, the annual cycle design can be viewed as a sequence of more or less autonomous stages, in which similar aims are achieved by means of a partially renewed and qualitatively improved training program. A test battery repeated at each stage, together with competitive performance results, will help to monitor the training process and provide feedback that can be used for ongoing evaluation and program corrections.

Finally, the number of training stages in an annual cycle depends on the particulars of the given sport and its calendar of important competitions which usually varies from four to seven. The typical annual cycle following the Block Periodization Concept is shown in Figure 1.9.

Practical implementation of the BPC has a number of benefits when compared to the traditional model:

- The Block Periodization model allows for a reduction in total mileage and time expended on training, without substantially changing the total number of workouts;
- Monitoring of trainedness is more purposeful and effective. The reduced number of targeted abilities requires more appropriate tests and the "dose-effect" analysis can be easily performed with respect to different training stages;
- Psychological traits are improved since the athletes can focus on fewer abilities. This allows for more effective maintenance of mental concentration and motivation levels.
- Nutritional aspects can be more carefully taken into account. A high protein diet can be given to enhance the anabolic effect of strength training while carbohydrates are particularly important in mesocycles for specialized and strength- endurance.

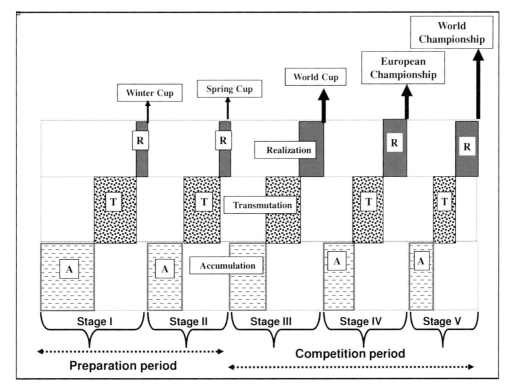

**Figure 1.9.** The annual cycle chart based on the Block Periodization
Concept (the transition period is not shown). The upper part refers to the
main competitions, the middle part to mesocycle-blocks and the bottom
part to training stages and preparation periods (Issurin, 2007).

## 1.3. Consequences of the modern approach

Table 1.8 summarizes the most relevant differences between the traditional
and non-traditional approaches to training periodization and the annual training plan.
The dominant principle focuses on the structure of the training workloads, where the
use of highly concentrated workloads contrasts with the complex administration of
various workloads in the traditional approach. The residual training effect concept is
part of the scientific background for the new approach but plays no part in the classic
plan, which was based exclusively on the cumulative training effect. In addition,
development of a wide range of abilities required simultaneous training in the classic
approach, but is strictly consecutive in the block-structure.

The term "periodization" (preparation periods) itself reflects the most
meaningful component of the classic approach. As mentioned earlier, the most
meaningful component in the alternative approach is the training stage that consists of

*Key: Residual Training Effect.*

31

three sequenced mesocycle-blocks. Unlike the traditional model, the BPC allows for successful implementation of a multi-peak annual plan. The intermediate peaks can be planned for mid-season and even for the early part of the season.

The general physiological mechanism of adaptation is very different when the two training plans are compared. The traditional model exploits mainly adaptation to concurrent training stimuli affecting many abilities while the non-traditional model (BPC) assumes superimposition of residual training effects induced by highly concentrated training stimuli administered consecutively.

*Concurrent -*
*Occurring or existing simultaneously or side by side*

**Table 1.8**

**Principal differences in training design between the classic approach and BPC**

**(Issurin, 2007)**

| Characteristics of the training design | Traditional model | Block Periodization model |
|---|---|---|
| Dominant workload structure | The complex use of different workloads directed at many abilities | The use of highly concentrated workloads directed at a minimum number of abilities |
| Scientific basis for the planning approach | Cumulative training effects | Cumulative and residual training effects |
| Sequencing of different abilities | Predominantly simultaneous | Predominantly consecutive |
| The main planning components | Periods of preparation, preparatory, competitive and transitory | Preparation includes and combines three types of mesocycle-blocks |
| Participation in competition | Predominantly in the competitive period | Predominantly at the end of each stage |
| General physiological mechanisms involved. | Adaptation to concurrent training stimuli affecting many different abilities | Superimposition of residual training effects induced by highly concentrated training stimuli |

*Superimposition: add or join*

## Summary

The traditional theory of training periodization was developed as a universal approach to the planning and preparation of athletes. The tremendous changes in high-level sport, as well as the dissemination of new training technologies, has led to an evolution of general theoretical positions and the appearance of several non-traditional coaching concepts. Training Block Periodization, the alternative to the traditional preparation approach, reflects the successful experience of many prominent coaches and the results of long-term studies conducted on top-level athletes.

The general idea behind the alternative approach is the use of sequenced specialized mesocycle-blocks, where highly concentrated training workloads are focused on a minimal number of motor and technical abilities. Unlike the traditional theory of training periodization that uses simultaneous development of many abilities, the alternative concept provides for consecutive development of the targeted abilities in successive mesocycle-blocks. The rational sequencing of these blocks is based on residual training effects, i.e., the retention of changes brought about by the training that remain after the training ceases. These training residuals are especially important when athletes improve their abilities consecutively, not concurrently as in the traditional model.

The Block Periodization Concept utilizes an original taxonomy of mesocycles that consist of three types of specialized blocks: *accumulation,* for developing basic motor and technical abilities (mostly aerobic and muscle strength abilities as well as basic technical skills); *transmutation,* for developing event-specific abilities (mostly anaerobic and/or aerobic-anaerobic abilities, and more specialized technical skills), and *realization*, for maximal speed, event-specific tactics and full adaptation prior the forthcoming trial or competition (this block is very similar to the widely-known concept of pre-event tapering). These three mesocycle-blocks, taken as a whole, form the training stage, that is, the most meaningful component of alternative training periodization. This contrasts to the classical scheme where the most meaningful component is the training period.

It should be noted that the traditional approach has visible benefits for the preparation of low- and mid-level athletes. The complex administration of workloads directed at many abilities makes training more diversified, attractive and lively. The improvement of relatively lower athletic abilities doesn't require highly concentrated training workloads because medium-level concentration still provides sufficient stimulation. The opposite situation is typical for high-level athletes who need high concentrations of appropriate exercises in order to make progress. Table 1.8 presents the main differences between the traditional and alternative training models.

The benefits of the Block Periodization Concept, in comparison to the traditional model, are as follows:

(1) the total volume of training exercises can be greatly reduced, minimizing the incidence of overtraining,

(2) the multi-peak training design allows for and facilitates successful participation in multiple competitions over the entire season;

(3) monitoring can be more efficient because of the substantial reduction in the number of athletic abilities to be evaluated within each mesocycle;

(4) the diet and restorative program can be appropriately modified according to the predominant type of training and, finally,

(5) a multi-stage annual plan creates more favorable conditions for peaking in time for the main competition of the season.

**References to Chapter 1**

Bompa, T. (1984). *Theory and methodology of training – The key to athletic performance*. Boca Raton, FL: Kendall/Hunt.

Bompa, T. (1999). *Periodization: Theory and methodology of training* (4th ed.). Champaign, IL: Human Kinetics.

Bondarchuk, A. P. (1986). *Training of track and field athletes*. Kiev: Health Publisher (Zdorovie).

Bondarchuk, A. P. (1988). Constructing a training system. Track Technique, 102, 3254-269.

Counsilman, B. E., & Counsilman, J.. (1991). The residual effects of training. *Journal of Swimming Research , 7,* 5-12.

Dick, F. (1980). *Sport training principles*. London: Lepus Books.

Harre, D. (Ed.). (1973). *Trainingslehre*. Berlin: Sportverlag

Fox, L.E., Bowers, R.W., Foss, M.L. (1993). *The physiological basis for exercises and sport*. Madison: Brown & Benchmark Publishers.

Issurin, V. (2003). *Aspekten der kurzfristigen Planung im Konzept der Blockstruktur des Training. Leistungsport, 33*, 41-44.

Issurin, V. (2007). A modern approach to high-performance training: the Block Composition concept. In: B.Blumenstein, R.Lidor, and G.Tenenbaum (Eds.), *Psychology of sport training* (pp. 216-234). Oxford: Meyer & Meyer Sport.

Issurin, V., Kaverin, V. (1985). *Planning and design of annual preparation cycle in canoeing*. In:"Grebnoj Sport" (Rowing, Canoeing, Kayaking), Moscow: Fizkultura i Sport, p. 25-29

Issurin, V., Kaverin, V., Nikanorov, A.N. et al. (1986). *Specialized preparation of canoe-kayak paddlers*. Moscow: State Committee of USSR for Physical Culture and Sport

Issurin, V., Shkliar, V. (2002). Zur Konzeption der Blockstuktur im Training von hochklassifizierten Sportlern. *Leistungsport, 6*, 42-45.

Issurin, V., Lustig G. (2004). Klassification, Dauer und praktische Komponenten der Resteffekte von Training. *Leistungsport. 34*, 55-59

Klausen, K. (1990). Strength and weight-training. In: Reilly T, Secher N., Snell P. and Williams C. (Eds.), Physiology of sports. London: E.&F.N.Spon, p.41-70.

Martin, D. (1980). *Grundlagen der Trainingslehre*. Schorndorf: Verlag Karl Hoffmann.

Matveyev, L.P. (1964). Problem of periodization in sports training. Moscow: Fizkultura i Sport.

Matveyev, L. (1977). *Fundamentals of sport training*. Moscow: Progress Publishers.

Ozolin, N. G. (1970). *The modern system of sport training*. Moscow: Fizkultura i Sport.

Steinacker, J. M. (1993). Physiological aspects of training in rowing. *International Journal of Sports Medicine, 14,* S3-S10.

Steinacker, J. M., Lormes, W., Lehman, M., and Altenburg, D. (1998). Training of rowers before world championships. *Medicine and Science in Sports and Exercise, 30,* 1158-63.

Suslov, F.P. (2001). Annual training programmes and the sport specific fitness levels of world class athletes. In: Annual Training Plans and the Sport Specific Fitness Levels of World Class Athletes. http://www.coachr.org/annual_training_programmes.htm

Thorstensson, A. (1988). Speed and acceleration. In A. Dirix, H. G. Knuttgen, & K. Tittel (Eds.), *The Olympic book of sports medicine. Encyclopedia of sports medicine* (Vol. I). Oxford: Blackwell Scientific Publications, p. 218-229.

Volkov N. (1986). Biochemistry of sport. In: Menshikov V. and Volkov, N. (Eds.), *Biochemistry*. Moscow: Fizkultura i sport, p.267-381.

Wilmore J. H., & Costill D. L. (1993). *Training for sport and activity. The physiological basis of the conditioning process.* Champaign, IL: Human Kinetics.

Yessis, M., with Trubo, R. (1987). *Secrets of Soviet Sports Fitness and Training*. New York: Arbor House.

Zatsiorsky, V. M. ( 1995). *Science and practice of strength training.* Champaign, IL: Human Kinetics.

# Chapter 2

Michael Kolganov
Olympic Bronze Medal Winner
Two-time World Champion in Kayaking
Israel

# Chapter 2

# The Workout
# General concepts and structure
# guidelines

Workouts are the smallest complete structural component of a training system. When joined and sequenced, workouts form the larger training cycles and stages. The current status of workouts is rather contradictory. On the one hand, coaches and athletes know how to structure single workouts in their sport. On the other hand, training approaches and preparatory schemes are constantly changing and improving. As a result, training workouts are modified as well. Some coaches reach a level of mastery in their creations, but frequently can not (or do not want to) explain how they compiled these sessions. The aim of this chapter is to present the most relevant general approaches to structuring the workout.

## 2.1 Workout types and classifications.

This section presents three practical and relevant workout classifications that deal with single training sessions in terms of their: (1) organization, (2) training tasks, and (3) load level.

## 2.1.1 Workouts according to organization

The many possible forms of organization used in world-wide coaching practice can be clustered into three basic categories. See Table 2.1.

**Table 2.1**

**Workouts classified according to their organization**

| Type | Form of organization | Possible benefits |
|------|---------------------|-------------------|
| Group workout | Collectively performed workout according to a strictly programmed or flexible plan | Team spirit, emotional, use of competitiveness and partnerships |
| Individual workout | Programmed workout managed by the coach | Focusing the coach's and athlete's attention on proper details of workload/technique |
| | Programmed workout managed by the athlete | Reduction of emotional strain, workout performed at convenient time and place |
| | Free or semi-free workout without strict plan | Free from self-initiative, self-regulation of load level |
| Mixed workout | Combination of first two organizational forms | Training diversity, possibility of combining benefits of the other forms |

As can be seen in Table 2.1, each form of organization and corresponding workout type has its specific benefits as well as its limitations. Group workouts as an organizational form, allow coaches to administer maximal workloads. This is the type most frequently used in training camps and in so-called centralized preparation, where a number of similarly ranked athletes train together. This is the prevailing form in team and combat sports. It should be noted that long-term preparation using group workouts exclusively clearly has psychological and neurophysiological limitations. When athletes train with high motivation, competitiveness and prolonged emotional strain, it can lead to excessive and chronic excitation of the central nervous system and eventually to emotional exhaustion. This is why it is essential to find a harmonious blend of strictly programmed team workouts here and in other types of workouts.

39

Individual workouts are used both for highly ambitious and strictly programmed training (as with the group training mentioned above) and for more liberal and less strenuous preparation. The use of individual workouts is greater in individual sports than in team and combat sports. In several sports like figure skating, individual workouts form almost the entire preparatory program of highly qualified athletes. Nevertheless, even in team sports, individual workouts contribute to the program of preparation as a whole. In soccer, basketball, ice hockey etc. pre-season preparation of world-class players is their own responsibility. World-class stars have to find their own facilities, coaching assistance and workout time-tables, which are usually individualized.

> **Example**. A highly successful, professional soccer player underwent a one-month specialized mesocycle for maximum speed during the off-season when 30-33 years old. He engaged a highly qualified track and field sprint coach, who planned, supervised and evaluated his training. The training cycle consisted of individual workouts managed by the coach and partly by the athlete. The focused work allowed the athlete to maintain a high level of speed despite difficulties caused by aging and previous injuries. (Mark Tunis, personal communication)

Mixed workouts are frequently used in many sports. In individual sports the individual part of the workout is usually used for perfecting technique, restoration and relaxation; in team and combat sports the individual parts of the workouts are usually devoted to conditioning training, acquisition of technical skills and relaxation.

> **Another example.** The legendary Edson Arantes Do Nascimento (Pele) said in an interview for a documentary, "Frequently I remained after the workouts and perfected shots, passes and playing with the head" ("Pele Forever", Directed by Anibal Massaini Neto, Brasilia, 2004). It would be fair to say that the combination of team-work and individual virtuosity was what made this sport genius so outstanding.

Many factors determine the proportions of the types of workouts to be employed. This includes sport specificity, training facilities, number of athletes being supervised by the coach, availability of individual instruments for self-supervision (like the Polar Watch, stoppers etc.), the possibility of combining indoor and outdoor exercises in one session, and each athlete's characteristics and preferences in terms of working in groups or individually.

## 2.1.2 Task related classification of workouts

Sports practice requires that we differentiate workouts in terms of prevalent tasks. A task related classification is presented in Table 2.2.

**Table 2.2**

**Task related classification of workouts**

| Type | Objectives | Notes |
|------|-----------|-------|
| Conditioning workouts | Improvement of motor abilities, general and/or sport specific motor fitness | This type is predominant in many sports and it is often combined with technical tasks |
| Technical workouts | Acquisition of new technical skills, perfection of movement technique | This type focuses on movement excellence and requires some indicators of quality |
| Tactical or techno-tactical workouts | Acquisition of new tactical (or techno-tactical) skills, perfection of individual and/or team tactics | Physical and mental exercises can be combined and theoretical sessions can be included as well |
| Workout-exams | Evaluation of athlete's abilities | Sport-specific competitive conditions can be simulated |
| Combined workouts | Developing various athletic abilities combining different tasks. | Options: 1) sequencing different workout types; 2) combining different tasks in certain exercises |

Conditioning workouts devoted to the development of general and sport-specific motor abilities form the major part of training programs in many sports. Very frequently these workouts include technical demands but without particular stress. Such workouts can be performed in different organizational formats, such as group or individual workouts managed by the coach or by the athletes themselves.

Technical workouts usually require more attention and organizational effort. The acquisition of new technical skills such as the perfection of movement technique, needs real-time evaluation and immediate correction in successive attempts.

Certainly, this work should be thoroughly controlled by the coach or specially engaged experts. However, most coaches in the U.S. are usually not proficient in the specifics of technique nor are there many experts in this area. Because of this it is important that they seek out valid sources for this information (Yessis, 2006). Individual self-managed workouts are not suitable for this purpose.

Thus, an additional factor affecting the complexity of technical workouts is the use of visual means such as videotapes in order to provide athletes with objective information about performance quality and meaningful details about proper technique. It should be emphasized that motor learning such as movement technique perfection, requires high mobilization of athletes' cognitive and coordinative abilities. Therefore, this workout type causes a particularly heavy load on the athletes' central nervous system that should be taken into account during planning.

Tactical or techno-tactical workouts are focused mostly on the acquisition of new tactical skills and the perfection of individual and/or team tactics. Another function of these workouts is to link tactical and technical skills, which is extremely important for successful performance. Several parts of tactical workouts can be practiced in sessions as part of theoretical and mental preparation. However, the major part of this work should be planned and thoroughly implemented in sport-specific conditions where stressful competitive situations can be partially simulated. This type of workout is more characteristic of team and combat sports, where the importance of tactics is relatively higher.

Workout tests are intended mainly to evaluate the athletes physical and technical abilities with regard to specially selected components of preparedness (sport-specific strength or endurance, etc.) or in artificially designed situations, which approach conditions in the forthcoming event as closely as possible. As these sessions demand maximal efforts from athletes, this type of workout should be carefully arranged and provided with the appropriate equipment in a suitable environment and with full cooperation of the coaching staff.

Combined workouts are devoted to developing a number of athletic abilities (e.g., physical and technical or physical and techno-tactical) within one workout. For example, the first part of a workout can be focused on motor learning while the second part is devoted to conditioning training. Similarly, a workout test can be followed by a conditioning workout. Another possibility for creating a combined workout is to link up different training tasks in special sport-specific exercises. This approach assumes simultaneous development of a sport-specific motor ability and perfection of appropriate technical skills. These combined training means, having a two-sided effect, are termed *conjugate exercises*. Usually such conjugation is provided in the form of speed resisted and speed assisted exercises (Maglischo, 1992). They can also be done with specialized strength exercises (Yessis, 2006)

*[handwritten margin note: Conjugate: Two-sided effect (Train multiple abilities)]*

> **Example** . Exercises with additional resistance are widespread and especially popular in cyclic type sports such as running, swimming, canoeing, rowing etc. Usually these exercises are directed towards improving force application within a sport-specific technical skill and enhancing appropriate muscular endurance. The speed resisted approach can usually be realized with the help of relatively inexpensive equipment. Speed assisted exercises are supposed to facilitate high speed regimes and often, to break the so-called "speed barrier". The combined effect of such drills is the enhancement of sport-specific speed technique and improvement of maximal speed or event-specific speed endurance.

## 2.1.3 Load related classifications

From the viewpoint of planning and training analysis, load-related differentiation of workouts is of particular importance. For practical purposes, it is necessary to enumerate three general functions of workouts: development, retention and restoration. The appropriate load level selected should correspond to these aims. In actual fact, each training plan is a specific combination of these workout types: some are intended to enhance development, others are necessary to retain certain capabilities at the previously attained level; and special sessions are planned for restoration. Therefore, the aim related workout load classification has practical value. Zatsiorsky's load-related classification (1995), presents quantified workouts on a scale of 1 to 5 where 1 represents the lowest load and 5 the highest, as seen in Table 2.3.

43

**Table 2.3**

**Quantification of workouts: Aim related load classification (based on Zatsiorsky, 1995; modified by Issurin, 2003)**

| Workout aim | Training load level | Restoration time, hours | Load assessment, Reference points. |
|---|---|---|---|
| Development | Extreme | > 72 | 5 |
| | Large | 48-72 | 4 |
| | Substantial | 24-48 | 3 |
| Retention | Medium | 12-24 | 2 |
| Restoration | Small | < 12 | 1 |

The load related aspects of this classification need additional clarification with regard to the desirable time for full restoration. The main limitation relates to workouts associated with considerable psychological and neuro-physiological effort. The classification presented above uses the time needed for full restoration as an objective indicator of load level. This approach pertains to strength, power, endurance, speed, etc. exercises. High-level coordination training and workouts that induce heightened neuro-emotional stress usually require less time for full restoration.

However, it is not always possible to select integrative objective markers and indicators based exclusively on the duration of restoration. Nevertheless, the generally approved approach assumes a series of several workouts, which corresponds to the desired load level according to pedagogical and sport specific estimations. For this purpose, Borg's widely used scale of perceived exertion (Borg, 1973) can be adapted to assess workouts according to their load level (Table 2.4).

**Table 2.4**

**Workout load levels using Borg's Rate of Perceived Exertion (author's modification)**

| RPE values | Load qualification | Type of workout |
|---|---|---|
| 6<br>7<br>8<br>9<br>10<br>11 | Very Very Easy<br><br>Very Easy<br><br>Fairly Easy | Restoration |
| 12<br>13<br>14 | Slightly Difficult | Retention |
| 15<br>16 | Difficult | Development – substantial load |
| 17<br>18 | Very Difficult | Development – large load |
| 19<br>20 | Very Very Difficult | Development – extreme load |

Following both of the above load-related classifications at least two practical and relevant consequences can be noted:

1) The load level of each workout can be quantified and expressed numerically. This can give additional planning benefits particularly in non-measurable sports (team sports, gymnastics etc.) and allow stronger emphasis on specially selected workouts;

2) Implementation of the load-dependent categories of development, retention, and restoration workouts allows for better differentiation between different training sessions and more precise selection of appropriate workloads.

## 2.1.4 Key-workouts as the decisive factor in developmental training sessions

The BPC (Block Periodization Concept) pays particular attention to the design of the training composed of several workouts. The principle of high concentration demands that training loads be focused on a minimal number of targeted abilities (see 2.2.2). Unlike the traditional training approach, where the total volume of exercises performed are of primary importance, the BPC postulates absolute priority of the total number of development workouts as the crucial factor.

---

**Example**. A highly qualified canoeist needs to develop basic aerobic endurance. For this purpose he has to perform a 40-45 km weekly volume of exercises at near- anaerobic threshold level. Following the traditional approach, this mileage can be divided among nine workouts, where these exercises will be combined with drills for other training modalities (anaerobic glycolitic endurance, strength endurance, maximal speed etc.). The athlete performing this program will be permanently fatigued and the training effect will be small to negligible.

The BPC requires concentration on target-specific exercises mostly within three-four development workouts that can not be combined with any anaerobic glycolitic tasks. The athletes will sometimes (but not always) be fatigued after strenuous development workouts, but the training effect will be more favorable.

---

According to the BPC, quality of training is determined strictly by the quantity and placement of development workouts. Moreover, some of the workouts should be especially stressed and carefully arranged through appropriate planning. The most important development workouts, which are focused on the current main training emphasis, are called "*key-workouts*".

For a long time, leading coaches have selected and emphasized workouts which create peak points of related training cycles and concentrate the most important tasks and workloads. Such peak sessions, recently renamed "key-workouts", require athletes to concentrate mentally and emotionally and to be ready to work harder than usual.

---

**Example**. Tim Noakes (1991), a well known sport physiologist, formulated a number of training rules based on the experiences of the greatest middle- and long-distance runners such as Herbert Elliott, Ron Clarke and Frank Shorter. The first one is: "Alternate hard and easy training days". This is very similar to the coaching concept of key-workout, which can be expressed as, "alternate particularly stressful workouts with less hard and easy sessions".

---

*[Handwritten margin notes: "HI-Low Method", "Doyle-Winter '07", "Rotate Load ↑Vol ↓o have hard and easy rotation"]*

46

The principle of workload concentration postulated for BPC should be implemented for several workouts as well. The basic characteristics of the key-workouts are presented in Table 2.5.

**Table 2.5**

**Basic characteristics and particulars of key-workouts**

| Basic characteristics | Particulars |
|---|---|
| Target ability | The most relevant abilities are targeted in this training cycle, usually one aimed at motor fitness, and one at technique or tactics |
| Mental factor | Motivation of athletes should be focused on a particular workout that strongly determines the effect of the whole training program |
| Timing | The key-workout is planned for the best time, when the athletes have adjusted to the preceding loads but are still not overly fatigued |
| Load level | Adjusted to the demands of the development workout or a substantial, large or extreme level |
| Organizational forms | Partnership, cooperation within a group and team spirit are particularly desirable |
| Training monitoring | Thorough and objective recording of relevant information using such instruments as chronometry, HR monitors, blood lactate, video, or using visual signs and pedagogical estimations |

*[handwritten note: → Must determine when this is.]*

As can be seen from Table 2.5, key-workouts require special attention in terms of methodology, organization and psychology. The sessions should contain the most effective and productive exercises since their results can often be utilized for training control and for estimating the athletes' work potential.

It is not recommended that key workouts include previously unknown training means or completely new conditions, which demand preliminary adjustment. Athletes should be focused on top quality in their work; new means and conditions can divert the athletes' attention from load-specific details and reduce motivation levels. All performance demands, organizational details and work conditions should be clearly explained prior the workout. This holds true for any training session but is particularly important in key-workouts.

*[handwritten note: → How testing is ran. Or heavy days.]*

*[handwritten note: ✳ Explain the workout to the guys.]*

## 2.2 Workout structure

Despite the variety and specificity of various sports, there are general rules about how each single workout should be structured. Knowledge of workout structure relates to the most comprehensive part of training theory, which all coaches begin to learn from their initial experiences in their athletic career. Indeed, everyone knows that a single workout consists of a *warm-up* (introductory part), *basic part* where planned workloads are performed, and *cool-down* (concluding part). This general structure pertains to all possible combinations of organizational forms and exercises and has been described by many authors. Nevertheless, progress in sports science and practice has led to a more complete understanding of the facts which once seemed very simple but now appear more sophisticated. Thus, the essence and content of each workout component can now be elucidated with greater clarity.

### 2.2.1 Warm-up

The great New Zealand coach Arthur Lydiard included a chapter on warm-up in his book with Garth Gilmour (2000). He mentioned that world renowned Australian coach Percy Cerutty, who had worked with multiple world record holder and Olympic running champion Herbert Elliott, was asked about the role of warm-up. The authoritative coach answered that rabbits don't warm-up but can run "like the very devil". The anonymous coach from Abilene College who had asked the question took this reply seriously and conducted a special study.

> **Case study.** The Abilene coach filmed a rabbit's behavior prior to its running activity. When rabbit came out from its burrow, it looked around (moving its head and stretching its neck and back muscles) and trotted forth and back several times. Afterwards the rabbit started to run across the field. Thus, the rabbit really performed a warm-up although not as seriously as human runners (Lydiard & Gilmour, 2000).

It would be fair to say that nowadays, very few coaches or athletes still doubt the necessity of warming up. However, examples of effective models and combinations are required. To this end, as is usual in high-performance training, two major approaches exist: summarizing experiences from around the world, and reviewing the outcomes of well designed studies. The second approach can be illustrated by the findings of a long-term study conducted with high-level athletes.

**Case study.** Twelve National division soccer teams (180 players) were subdivided into two groups. The first one used a modified training program where warm-ups and cool-downs were carefully conducted, based on the outcomes of previous studies. This included ball exercises combined with a stretching program and cool-downs that consisted of jogging and hold-relax stretching. The preparation was supervised by doctors and physiotherapists. The second group of six teams trained traditionally and served as the control. The results of a six month follow up revealed highly significant superiority for the modified preparation program (Figure 2.1). There was a four-fold reduction in the number of injuries and a drastic decrease in workouts and games missed due to musculoskeletal disorders (Ekstrand et al, 1983).

The above study can be considered atypical because it refers to the complex effects of warming-up, cooling-down and medical supervision. Usually the scientific approach deals with the separate effects of several factors and what their outcomes can contribute to practice. For instance:

- incorporating stretching exercises in the warm-up increases the range of motion of soccer players' lower extremities (Moller et al., 1985);

- active warm-up without stretching doesn't affect flexibility and is therefore insufficient (Zakas et al., 2006);

- prior intense exercise substantially stimulates aerobic metabolism in working muscles during subsequent strenuous performance (Bangsbo et al., 2001).

On the other hand, experiences in advanced sports practice remain a very valuable source for organizing warm-up in a particular sport.

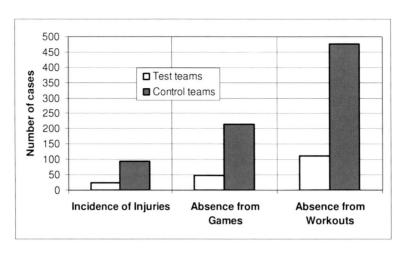

**Figure 2.1** Prevention of soccer injuries as a result of a modified training program that focused on warm-up and cool-down (based on Ekstrand et al., 1983)

The warm-up, as an introductory part of each workout, has three general functions: metabolic adjustment, technical and coordination adjustments, and mental readiness (Table 2.6). Metabolic adjustment should be sport-specific.

However, it does not mean that the warm-up is important only for certain athletes, as for example, runners and not for shooters. In fact, the thermal and energy changes are absolutely necessary for subsequent serious work even though the character and content of these actions are sport-specific. The important role of metabolic adjustment in preventing musculoskeletal damages should also be mentioned. Interviews with prominent coaches in various sports reveal that at least half of the musculoskeletal injuries (low-back, shoulders, knees, ankles etc.) are partially or completely caused by insufficient warm-up. On the other hand, adequate accommodation of appropriate metabolic systems strongly determines the effectiveness of subsequent workloads in the main part of a workout.

## Table 2.6

### The main functions, objectives and expected effects of warm-up

(based on deVries, 1986; McArdle, Katch & Katch, 1991; Powers & Howley, 1994).

| Function | Objectives | Expected effects |
|---|---|---|
| Metabolic adjustment | To accommodate all metabolic systems for subsequent efforts and to prevent musculoskeletal damage to non warmed-up tissues | Elevation of muscle and core temperature, viscosity of muscles and resistance of the vascular bed decrease with heating, hemoglobin and myoglobin link up more oxygen, oxygen uptake increases |
| Technique and coordination adjustment | To activate the central and peripheral nervous systems and to prevent injuries due to failure in highly coordinated skills | Muscles contract and relax faster, muscle perception and all motor control links are enhanced, basic biomechanical characteristics and movement technique become more stable and economical |
| Attainment of mental readiness | To mobilize the athlete or group for conscientious work, to attain appropriate motivation for certain tasks | Attainment of mental concentration on forthcoming workloads and improvement of mental and emotional self-control |

Technique and coordination adjustment is an indispensable function of warm-up in any sport. The role it plays in preventing injuries will be considered below in detail. A third function of warm-up is also essential and its importance is particularly high in sports and workouts where mental and cognitive components play the leading role, such as in team and combat sports. It is acquisition of new technical skills etc.

Warm-up in any sport is subdivided into two parts, general and specific. They are characterized by a corresponding selection of exercises (Table 2.7).

Explain training

The general part of warm-up usually starts with setting goals for the forthcoming workout. This is the time when the most substantial details of workloads and training organization should be explained. High-performance athletes usually have their own style of warming-up, hence they perform their standard combination of exercises. Nevertheless, sometimes several details of the general workout should be → Actual Dyn. accentuated, as for example, prolonging the general part due to lower external Flex. temperature (simply stated, cool athletes need more time to warm up). It may include additional exercises because of previously injured muscles or joints, more careful exercising of specific muscle groups that are still painful after the preceding training session, etc. Indications of the desirable state that should be induced by this part of workout are increased heart rate (up to 110-130 b/min), slight perspiration, increased breathing frequency and pulmonary ventilation and improvement of the overall body state. The general warm-up usually lasts 8-15 min.

**Table 2.7**

**General and special parts of warm-up**

| Part | Content | Particulars |
|---|---|---|
| General | Low- and medium-intensity cyclic exercises (running, jogging, skipping etc.), calisthenics – various exercises with full range of motion involving major muscle groups and all joints done mostly without additional weight or resistance | Can be performed individually or in small groups; duration about 8-15 min depending on external temperature and individual demands |
| Special | Sport-specific exercises affecting mainly the predominant metabolic systems and technical (and/or techno- tactical) skills to be engaged in the main part of the workout | Can be performed under the coach's supervision-- duration about 10-20 min |

The initial part of warm-up should usually include a few low- and medium-intensity exercises in order to raise blood circulation, increase body temperature and facilitate the oxidation processes in working muscles. It is commonly believed that warmed muscles and connective tissues are more easily extended and respond positively to stretching exercises. Thus, the next step includes stretching exercises where active dynamic stretching (swings, arm and upper body rotations etc.) precede passive stretching. The general warm-up continues with moderate effort strength exercises usually performed without more weight, although exercises with a partner's resistance can be utilized.

The special part of warm-up is very focused on sport-specific metabolic and/or technical particulars of the forthcoming workout. The specially selected drills should activate the coordination mechanisms that are involved in the technical skills used in the main (basic) part of the workout. In addition, these exercises should assist in stimulating mental readiness for subsequent motor tasks of higher complexity. These exercises are important for preventing failure in highly coordinated skills and, therefore, they contribute to preventing injuries.

Despite the variety of possible warm-up versions, two alternative modes exist and are practiced by creative coaches in various sports (Table 2.8).

**Table 2.8**

**Two alternative modes of special warm-up prior to the workout**

| Mode | Content | Benefits |
|------|---------|----------|
| Standard warm-up | Completely standardized program using accustomed to exercises and tasks in a specific sequence | Performance economy, relatively short duration, simple organization |
| Non-standard warm-up | Modeled pre-event warm-up or another non-standard plan including relatively new or attractive elements | Breaking routine, fine tuning for extraordinary forthcoming program |

The most frequently used mode is the *standard special warm-up* comprised of accustomed to exercises and tasks in a specific sequence. Such a warm-up is a part of a routine which needs no additional motivation, and is simply organized lasting 8-15 min. Highly qualified athletes usually have their own standardized warm-up and even a number of appropriate versions for event-specific needs.

**Example**. Weightlifters perform an individually standardized special warm-up for the snatch and another for the clean and jerk. The content and duration of these variants is individually tailored by the athlete and coach. Gymnasts use special warm-up for each gymnastics event like rings, floor exercise, vault, parallel bars etc. Of course, the relatively constant content and duration of these warm-ups is modified depending on external factors (temperature, humidity etc.) and internal conditions (fatigue, previous injury, anxiety etc.).

A *particular special warm-up* tends to emphasize the extraordinary character of further work. This can be a specially arranged workout test where a quasi-competitive situation is stressed. Correspondingly, the modified pre-event warm-up can be managed. The extraordinary key-workout can also be preceded by a particular warm-up that is intended to stress the exclusive character of this session. Similarly, extraordinary events like local festivals; public presentations etc. can be the reasons for using a particular warm-up. It is worth noting that frequent utilization of a particular warm-up leads to a loss of its uniqueness and reduces its stimulatory effect.

## 2.2.2 The basic (main) part of the workout

The basic part of the workout is sometimes called the "loading phase" because it concentrates all the real workloads planned for the session. Thus, the desired acute responses from the athletes should be attained here as a result of properly selected and correctly performed exercises and tasks. These responses can be characterized by objective indicators of the cardiovascular system (heart rate), metabolic state (blood lactate), emotional tension (galvanic skin response), performance estimates (speed, performance time, movement rate etc.), and subjective signs of effort and/or fatigue (rate of perceived exertion etc.). Each of these indicators can reflect the general attainment and maintenance of the highest level for this session. The basic part is the longest one in the workout and usually lasts about 60-90 min. Of course, during this time interval, the load level should be properly adjusted.

Depending on sport specificity, the basic part of the workout can contain a large number of exercises (as in track and field, swimming or gymnastics) or just one task (such as a match in team sports). For a long time, prominent coaches in different sports strived to structure workouts by selecting and emphasizing the most important exercise or task. The coaches termed this "the meaningful exercise", "the chief link of the workout", "the main task", "the highlight of the program" etc.

> **Example**. A few decades ago the great track and field coach Arthur Lydiard offered a number of weekly programs for different running events and ages (Lydiard & Gilmour, 2000). These programs offered only one exercise in each workout. Obviously, a workout program for runners does not contain only one exercise; what Lydiard did was to pinpoint only the most important one. Similarly, typical weekly training reports of great running stars display one exercise in each workout which means that the athletes report only on exercises or drills of primary importance (Noakes, 1991)

From the viewpoint of block training, the emphasis on key-function exercises/drills is very characteristic. Following the principle of training workload concentration (1.2.2) the accentuation of a specially selected exercise is logical and desirable. Following the principle of a minimum number of targeted abilities, one selected exercise or task is usually accentuated. Similar to the definition of key-workout, the main meaningful element of the workout is termed the *key-exercise*. In several sports such as team or combat sports, where the key-function frequently belongs not to a given exercise, but to a sport-specific task (training match, training fight, etc.) the most important workload is the *key-task*. The major characteristics and particulars of key-exercises (tasks) are presented in Table 2.9.

**Table 2.9**

**The major characteristics and particulars of key-exercises (tasks) in a workout**

| Major characteristics | Particulars | Comments |
|---|---|---|
| Targeted exercises | Correspond to the main target (objective) of a given workout | Usually only one key-exercise (task) should be selected |
| Motivation | It requires maximal self-motivation and maximum moral support of the coach | Athletes should be familiar with the key-exercise (task) in order to generate the desired mental concentration |
| Timing | The best "prime-time" is assigned, when athletes are in the most favorable state | High athlete sensitivity allows them to better respond to the workload |
| Organization | Performance details like interaction of partners, equipment, access to information etc. should be properly provided | Meaningful details (directions, drafting, game scenario etc.) strongly determine the acute effect of the key-exercise (task) |
| Monitoring | The most relevant performance variables are recorded by the coach or his/her assistant | It's important to provide each athlete with relevant exercise-specific information |

The concept of key-exercise can be illustrated by a case study conducted during the preparation of Gal Friedman, gold medal winner in the sailing regatta at the Athens Olympic Games (Figure 2.2).

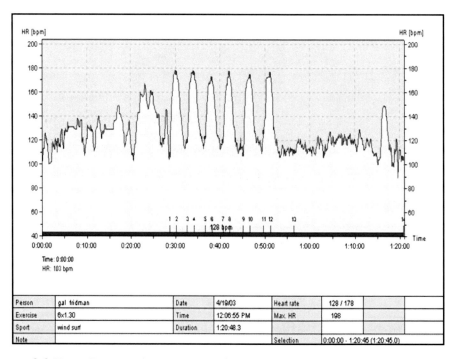

**Figure 2.2** Heart Rate workout pattern of Gal Friedman, gold medal winner in the windsurfing regatta at the Athens Olympic Games.

Key-exercise, 6×1.5min pumping with 1.5min rest (by courtesy of Omrit Yanilov-Eden, 2005).

**Case study**. Gal Friedman, a world-leading windsurfer, substantially reformed the traditional training approach which was based mostly on extensive long-duration workouts at sea. He initiated highly intense interval workouts, in which high efforts were produced through forceful pumping movements. In this, the athlete produced propulsion by frequent flaps of the sail. The typical key-exercise performed by Gal was as follows: 6 repetitions of speed movements for 1.5 minutes with 1.5 min intervals of low intensity movement (Figure 2.2). The speed regime of each performance was controlled, and an HR monitor was used to evaluate the athlete's response. The graph displays repetitive HR peaks at the 178 level with subsequent reduction to 110 b/min, while his personal HR maximum was 198. Thus, the planned key-exercise was executed at 90% of his personal HR upper limit. This load level was definitely the highest in the entire workout (Yanilov-Eden, 2005)

56

Selection of the key-exercise is of primary importance in structuring a workout and offers a professional challenge for coaches. Despite the illusory simplicity of this operation, many mistakes have been made in routine work, even by experienced coaches.

**Example**. At a national coaching seminar attended by representatives who had earned many Olympic, World and Continental medals, participants were asked to put together a typical workout to develop certain motor abilities. Of the great variety of answers received, more than 50% were incorrect. Even experienced coaches confused exercises for maximal speed and speed endurance (anaerobic glycolitic capacity), exercises for aerobic endurance and aerobic power, etc. Apparently, it was time to refresh this basic knowledge.

Describing typical key-exercises for use in any sport is an unrealistic task. Nevertheless, it is possible to characterize the most typical training regimes of key-exercises to develop major motor abilities (Table 2.10).

**Table 2.10**

**Characteristics of key-exercises for developing major motor abilities**

**(based on Fox & Mathews,1981 and Viru, 1995 with author's modification)**

| Targeted-ability | Work interval | Work/rest ratio | Intensity | Number of repetitions | Number of series | Blood lactate, HR |
|---|---|---|---|---|---|---|
| Maximal speed | 7-15s | 1: 10 | Maximal | 5-8 | 2-5 | - |
| Anaerobic glycolitic power | 30-50s | 1: (4-5) | Submaximal | 4-6 | 2-4 | > 8 > 180 |
| Anaerobic glycolitic endurance | 1-1.5 min | 1:3 | High | 8-12 | 1-3 | Maximal > 8 > 180 |
| Aerobic power | 1-2 min | 1: (1-0.5) | Intermediate | 5-8 | 1-3 | 4-8 160-180 |
| Aerobic endurance | 1-8 min | 1: 0.3 | Medium | 4-16 | 1-3 | 2.5-4 (5) 140-160 |
| Restoration, fat oxidation | 20-90 min | - | Low | 1-3 | - | 1-2.5 100-140 |

The format of this chapter and entire book does not allow a thorough consideration of the above schematic description of key-exercises. In addition, very important strength exercises for many sports are not touched on here. For these, many other sources in the literature can be recommended. Nevertheless, the general rules highlighted here, irrespective of sport, can assist coaches in structuring their own version of key-exercises and workouts as a whole.

### 2.2.3 Cooling down

The last, but still compulsory part of each single workout is intended to reduce load level gradually and normalize basic functions in the body. It is called the *cool-down*. Its specific objectives are:

- to reduce body temperature, heart rate and blood pressure back to resting levels;
- to remove acid metabolites and other waste products from the muscles to the circulatory system for further clearance;
- to facilitate recovery of the endocrine system first, by reducing adrenaline and noradrenaline levels in order to prevent restlessness and sleep disorders at night;
- to reduce emotional tension and affect athletes' mental recovery in a positive way.

Generally speaking, the cool-down is both an influencing factor and a relevant condition for effective restoration of the athlete. Despite its obvious importance there have been many cases in which this indispensable part of the workout has been ignored, even by successful high-performance athletes. Usually a lack of time is cited as the reason for such mistaken behavior. The previously mentioned study of professional soccer players (Figure 2.2) has shown the role of rational warm-up and cool-down in protecting the athletes' health. As further support, the following study outcomes can be cited.

**Case study**. Forty-eight adult soccer players were subdivided into three groups that were tested with respect to range of motion (ROM) in the lower extremities before, immediately after, and 24 h after different types of workouts. The regular soccer workout caused a significant decrease in all ROM indices. A similar workout that included a stretching series in warm-up induced more favorable responses immediately after the session. The third version, in which the stretching series was inserted in the cool down, provided significant benefits in ROM immediately after the workout and 24 h later. The authors stressed that tight muscles with reduced ROM predisposed the athletes to a higher risk of injuries (Moller et al., 1985).

In general, the cool-down repertory can be subdivided into three categories: (1) low intensity exercises, usually slow locomotions like jogging, walking, swimming etc., (2) breathing and relaxation exercises and (3) stretching exercises. The particulars of these activities are summarized in Table 2.11.

The common pattern of cool-down usually starts with slow locomotion that leads to elimination of waste products from the muscles. It has long been known that such activity facilitates recovery and causes faster lactate removal from the athlete's muscles (Bonen & Belcastro, 1976). It is known that highly intense and prolonged exercises cause a decrease in circulating blood volume due to water accumulation in intra- and extra-cellular compartments of the muscles (Sejersted et al., 1986). Recovery of the water-electrolyte balance may take a long time. In extreme cases (marathon running, for instance) it can reach two or more days (Viru, 1995). An effecitve cool-down procedure can profoundly accelerate this process.

**Table 2.11**

**Types and expected effects of various cool-down activities**

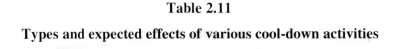

| Types of activity | Expected effects | Comments |
|---|---|---|
| Low intensity exercises | Reduction in body temperature, heart rate and blood pressure; removal of blood lactate and other acid metabolites, a decrease in adrenaline and noradrenaline levels and normalization of blood volume and electrolytic balance | This activity is particularly desirable after highly intense exercises, team and dual sport matches, fights in combat sports and exhausting long races |
| Breathing and relaxation exercises | Gradual decrease in pulmonary ventilation, reduction of excitation of the central nervous system, facilitated recovery of previously active muscle groups and a decrease in emotional tension | Combined breathing-relaxation exercises can accompany jogging or skipping and muscle shaking, can be performed in pairs |
| Stretching exercises | Reduction of training induced stiffness and tightness of muscles, lengthening of previously shortened muscles, increase in muscle and connective tissue elasticity and enhancement of flexibility | These exercises are particularly desirable after plyometric activities, which often elicit delayed onset muscle soreness |

*Catecholamines*
*Dopamine, adrenaline (epinephrine), and noradrenaline (norepinephrine)*
*·Released by adrenal medulla, of adrenal gland in response to stress.*

Restoration of the endocrine system is a more prolonged process and takes varying amounts of time according to each hormone. Exhausting workouts cause pronounced secretion of catecholamines (adrenaline and noradrenaline), that decrease rapidly in the restoration period (Hagberg et al., 1979; Jezova et al.,1985). Nevertheless, in extreme cases like the marathon and triathlon, increased catecholamine levels can remain for 24 hours and even more (Viru,1995). The increased post-exercise level of catecholamines can cause a number of negative effects like restlessness, sleep disorders etc. A rational cool-down can prevent or at least diminish these unfavorable responses in athletes.

Breathing and relaxation exercises can be performed independently of other activities or they can be combined with slow jogging, walking or swimming. The independent option can be done in drills such as breathing deeply with subsequent relaxation of upper body muscles combined with accentuated expiration. Active arm and leg relaxation can be performed while sitting or lying with the help of a partner

*Like vibration on Power Plate.*

*↑*

who shakes the relaxed extremity at varied frequencies and amplitudes. The combined option can be realized by jogging while breathing deeply and shaking the arms or legs.

Stretching exercises have frequently been indicated as the primary and most important component of cool-down. Special emphasis has been placed on their role in eliminating post-exercise muscle stiffness and tightness, and enhancing muscle and connective tissue elasticity (Shrier & Gossal, 2000). It is commonly believed that stretching can prevent delayed onset muscle soreness that is especially common following exercises having strong eccentric muscle contractions (so called plyometric exercises). This belief is supported by several studies (Hartfield, 1985) and contradicted by others (High et al., 1989).

In any case, the role of stretching exercises in preventing muscle injuries is generally considered to be very important. The stretching protocol is varied and sport-specific. Nevertheless, prominent coaches in different sports recommend performing static stretching and so called hold-relax exercises (passive muscle lengthening with subsequent relaxation) first. These can be followed by dynamic ballistic stretching exercises.

The total duration of cool-down depends on the character and amount of the preceding workload. For instance, blood lactate removal after a 4-min exhausting time trial requires about 20 min of restoration (Juel at al., 1990). This time span corresponds approximately to the cool-down duration. However this time period can be insufficient when the workout consists of a number of high intensity anaerobic sets. Cooling down usually lasts about 10-20 minutes which is not enough after sessions with extreme workloads.

## 2.3 Guidelines for constructing a workout

How each single workout is put together is up to the coach's creativity. Every coach develops his/her own style based on personal experiences and accumulated knowledge. Therefore, there are a variety of versions even within a given sport. At the same time a number of general guidelines can be offered irrespective of the sport. They are highlighted below.

### 2.3.1 Sequencing exercises for different training modalities

The BPC postulates a reduction in the number of targeted abilities that can be developed simultaneously. However, a unidirectional training design is the privilege of only a few sports where the number of abilities is limited (for instance, weightlifting does not require the development of many abilities; maximal and explosive strength are dominant and various modes of endurance are unnecessary). In other cases, there is a sequencing of different workloads within a single workout. From this viewpoint it is important to determine which exercises are preferable for the initial part and which belong in other parts of the workout. The general approach to this choice is based on the physiological demands of various exercises taking into account the optimal conditions for best performance (Figure 2.3).

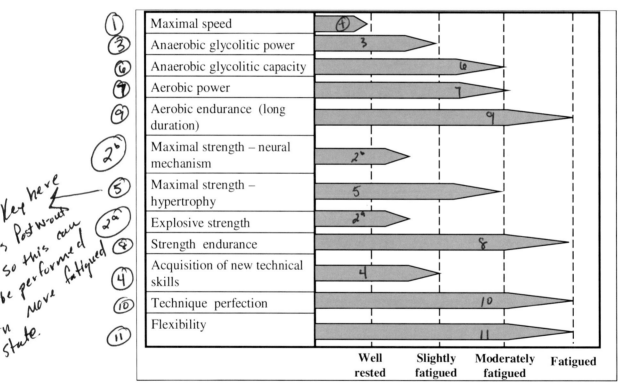

**Figure 2.3** The preferred physical states for different training modalities with regard to fatigue level within a single workout.

As can be seen from the above diagram, several targeted abilities can be successfully developed when the athlete is well rested or slightly fatigued. These include motor tasks, that require the central nervous system (CNS) to be in an optimal state. Exercises for maximal speed, explosive strength, acquisition of new technical skills, and drills to improve neural mechanisms of maximal strength (1-3 RM) require appropriate excitatory neural outputs that are not available in fatigued athletes. In additon, fatigued athletes can not respond effectively to these workloads due to inhibitory output from the CNS. Similarly, highly intense exercises for anaerobic glycolitic power assume the availability of sufficient energy resources, which are reduced in fatigued athletes. Exercises for anaerobic glycolitic capacity (speed endurance) demand sustained fatigue despite pronounced accumulation of acid metabolites in muscles and blood. Therefore, a certain level of fatigue is expected and even planned.

The acute effect of aerobic power workloads depends on the total duration of exercises performed close to maximum oxygen uptake levels. Moderately fatigued athletes can still sustain this metabolic level and, therefore, such dosages can be recommended. Similarly, the acute effect of hypertrophy strength training depends on the total amount of degraded muscle protein (rate of catabolism) and the magnitude of mechanical work performed (Zatsiorsky, 1995). Hence, a large amount of high resistance effort is required and, obviously, the last part of these workloads is performed when athletes are fatigued (but not exhausted).

---

**Example**. Imagine an athlete who performs a large volume of endurance exercises but needs to maintain his level of muscle mass and strength (this is very typical in endurance sports). The problem is to find appropriate time for the anabolic strength workout so that it will not interfere with the dominant aerobic work and will not detract from fine movement technique. It was recommended that the coach planned this workout after the medium load endurance session and when he did this, he was very surprised. He knew that maximum strength workouts demand "prime time" of rested athletes. This is actually correct, but only for strength exercises intended to enhance neural mechanisms (such as 1-3RM). Another goal of the workout is to attain muscle hypertrophy (like 8-10RM), where the crucial factor is not the athlete's state before the workout, but recovery conditions after the workout in order to provide the anabolic effect. Hence, such sequencing is reasonable and acceptable in practice.

---

Exercises for strength endurance and aerobic endurance demand sustained efforts despite accumulated fatigue and should therefore be continued as long as possible. The general rule is that motor learning demands an optimal state of the CNS and energy resourses. However, several technical features can be improved in highly exhausting workloads. For instance, fatigue tolerance of motor skill, movement economy and technique stability in unfavorable fatigue conditions can be enhanced only in an appropriate state which should be consciously programmed. Hence, some part of technique perfection can be performed by fatigued athletes. Similarly, stretching exercises are recommended for use in any part of the workout. It can be at the beginning as a part of warm-up, in the middle as active restoration and for improving flexibility, and at the end as a component of cool-down.

Exercise sequencing within the workout is strongly dependent on a clearly defined dominant ability targeted for the session. It in turn determines the content and placement of the key-exercise. Sometimes even small variations in the exercise order can modify and even suppress the expected acute effect. This can be illustrated using for example, high-resistance training, an indispensable part of the program for many sports.

---

**Case study**. Nine resistance trained male athletes performed the back squat (4 sets at 85% of 1RM) following two different protocols on separate days. Protocol "A" prescribed performing the squat during the initial part of the workout; protocol "B" required performing this exercise after a whole-body resistance exercise session (i.e., hang pull). Protocol "A" resulted in a significantly higher number of repetitions performed (8.0±1.9 compared with 5.4±2.7 in protocol "B"). However the average power in each set was higher in protocol "B" in comparison to performing the squats first. The authors attributed this phenomenon to postactivation potentiation induced by the preceding whole-body power exercise (Spreuwenberg et al., 2006). Thus, coaches who wish to elicit maximum hypertrophy should plan this exercise for the initial part of workout. If the main target is developing maximum power, this key-exercise should be planned after appropriate whole-body resistance exercises.

---

## 2.3.2 Compatibility of different exercises

The compatibility of various exercises with different training modalities within a single workout and within a workout series, is an extremely important factor that determines acute and immediate training effects. Negative interaction of several immediate training effects is one of the typical disadvantages of the traditional periodization system. Indeed, the complex approach to training design assumes the administration of exercises with different training modalities in a single workout. For a long time prominent coaches in most sports criticized and refused to implement this approach for high-performance training. The Block Periodization system utilizes a selective but not complex approach to each single workout in which carefully selected training modalities in compatible combinations are planned.

Figure 2.4 displays the main compatible combinations of dominant training modalities with several additional ones in a single workout.

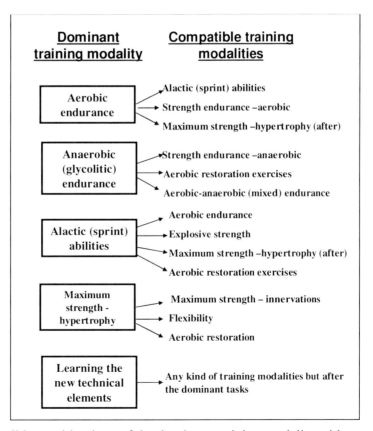

**Figure 2.4** Compatible combinations of the dominant training modality with additional ones in a single workout (Issurin, 2003).

The compatible combinations need to be clarified:

1) According to the BPC, the workout program should contain no more than three training modalities (usually one dominant, the second one – compatible with the main purpose, the third one – a modality of technique/tactic improvement or restoration);

2) It is postulated that 65-70% of the entire training time for the development workout should be devoted to one or two selected training modalities. This condition is important for attaining high workload concentration and to produce sufficient stimulus for a desirable training effect;

3) The typical frequency of workouts in high-performance training (6-12 a week) dictates certain conditions pertaining to the session subsequent to the key-workout. In the basic approach to training design there is a significant reduction in workload after the key-workout. The alternative approach, in which two consecutive key-workouts are planned, provides very high load concentrations which can be excessive;

4) Workouts for muscle hypertrophy impose very special demands when planning consecutive sessions within the restoration period. The use of high workloads during this period adversely affects the anabolic phase of muscle restoration and eliminates the hypertrophy process. Thus, to attain the anabolic effect it is necessary to substantially reduce workloads for at least 20 hours and to utilize appropriate restoration means;

5) Limiting the number of training modalities is particularly relevant in high-performance sport. For example, the daily program for juniors may be more diverse, multilateral and, therefore, more attractive.

It is worth noting that reasonably combined exercises allow coaches to emphasize the acute effect of the dominant training modality and/or to exploit the effect of previous exercises in subsequent workloads. A number of these favorable psycho-physiological interactions is shown in Table 2.12.

*[handwritten margin note: Part of reason high level ol only do a small # of different lifts.]*

66

**Table 2.12**

**Typical compatible combinations of different training modalities and psycho-physiological factors that create a beneficial interaction of combined workloads**

| Compatible combinations of training modalities | Psycho-physiological factors affecting load interaction |
|---|---|
| Aerobic endurance – alactic sprint ability | Brief sprint bouts break the monotony and sprinting recruits a wide spectrum of muscle fibers that remain activated during subsequent aerobic workloads |
| Aerobic endurance – strength endurance | The increased oxidation can be exploited in strength exercises and a combination of conventional and resistance exercises enriches the training program. |
| Anaerobic (glycolitic) endurance – anaerobic strength endurance | The glycolitic capacity can be effectively used by combining speed assisted, conventional and high resistance exercises. The mental factors in lactate tolerance are subject to augmented impact |
| Alactic sprint ability – explosive strength | Explosive strength components (jumps, throws, strokes etc.) used in alactic work intervals accentuate motor output |
| Maximum strength - flexibility | Stretching exercises facilitate muscular and mental relaxation, which can be exploited for active restoration in maximum strength workouts |
| Maximum strength – aerobic exercises | Low intensity aerobic exercises activate metabolic recovery and muscular and mental relaxation. This is useful for restoration during and after the strength workout |

### 2.3.3 One day workout series

The planning and execution of a number of workouts each day is widely used and commonly accepted in the preparation of high-performance athletes. Anecdotal reports by several prominent coaches indicate that four, five and even six daily workout series are successfully performed. A six daily workout series would be an exception but a two- and three-workout series is routine in training camp practice. Practical experiences in training design, control and follow up of daily workout series are extensive and objective data are available in the scientific literature. Most of the large amount of empirical data and previously presented scientific background (2.3.2) about how to construct daily series of workouts, however, are directed to developing aerobic abilities (Figure 2.5) or anaerobic abilities (Figure 2.6).

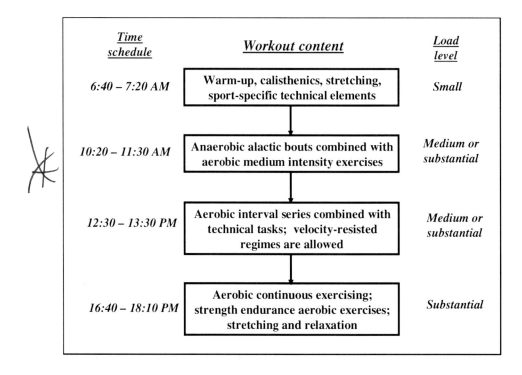

| Time schedule | Workout content | Load level |
|---|---|---|
| 6:40 – 7:20 AM | Warm-up, calisthenics, stretching, sport-specific technical elements | Small |
| 10:20 – 11:30 AM | Anaerobic alactic bouts combined with aerobic medium intensity exercises | Medium or substantial |
| 12:30 – 13:30 PM | Aerobic interval series combined with technical tasks; velocity-resisted regimes are allowed | Medium or substantial |
| 16:40 – 18:10 PM | Aerobic continuous exercising; strength endurance aerobic exercises; stretching and relaxation | Substantial |

**Figure 2.5** Daily workout series devoted mostly to aerobic ability development (with additional compatible training modalities – alactic ability and strength endurance)

The ultimate purpose of subdividing the total daily amount of exercises into three, four or more workouts is to increase the quality of training, i.e., the intensity of exercises and their partial volume, the creation of more favorable conditions for restoration, and to benefit more from technique improvement in relatively better restored athletes, etc.

Consider the daily series for aerobic development (Figure 2.5). The first workout contains gradually increasing workloads. Very often athletes suffer from stiffness and soreness of muscles and thus, the light early morning workout helps to reduce these negative consequences of previous workloads and to prepare them for further serious work. The appropriate technical elements can activate sport-specific sensations and facilitate motor control.

The second workout provides favorable conditions for sprints, which interact positively with moderately intense aerobic drills. A one hour break before the third workout restores the athletes for a more concentrated aerobic program. Three hours of rest prior to the final session of the day readies them to perform continuous aerobic drills and the aerobic resistance program, despite the fatigue accumulated during previous work throughout the day. The cool-down program is particularly important in this workout and usually takes relatively more time.

In highly intense training, the time between the daily exercise sessions is of particular importance (Figure 2.6).

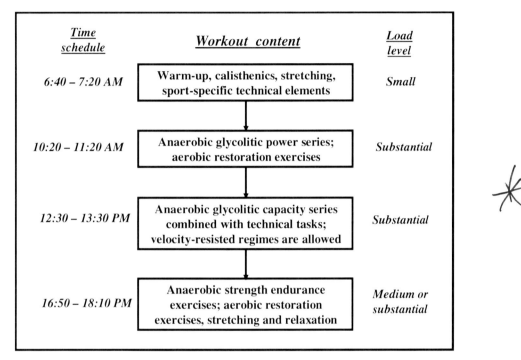

**Figure 2.6.** Daily workout series devoted mostly to anaerobic power and anaerobic capacity development (with an additional compatible training modality – anaerobic strength endurance)

The first workout in a daily series is similar to the example described previously except that brief intense efforts can be included. The second workout contains highly intense aerobic power exercises that produce fast accumulation of acid metabolites and oxygen debt. The one hour break before the third workout provides partial restoration during which about 70-80% of the accumulated lactate can be oxidized (Volkov, 1986). Nevertheless the next session starts when athletes are slightly fatigued. It is worth noting that the glycolitic pathway and enzymatic pool are still activated by the preceding workout. This positively affects the second highly intense workout with its exercises for anaerobic glycolitic capacity (anaerobic endurance).

The three hour break following the third workout provides the athletes with partial restoration, although the athletes come to the fourth and final workout fatigued. Consequently, the warm-up and cool-down parts can be markedly prolonged. In the basic part of the session, the anaerobic strength endurance exercises, which entail sustaining progressive fatigue, can be successfully performed. Hence, the daily workout series facilitates an increase in the total amount of anaerobic glycolitic exercises and the attainment of a more profound metabolic response.

The one day workout series can be structured with regard to various ability-targets such as maximum speed, explosive strength or techno-tactical abilities in combat sports. It should be noted that the four-workout series under consideration is not as widely practiced as the two a day workout program that is routine in high-performance training. The most typical compatible combinations of two sequenced workouts per day are presented in Table 2.13.

**Table 2.13**

**Typical combinations of compatible training modalities in two workouts per day (key-exercises are noted)**

| Dominant targeted ability | First workout | Second workout |
|---|---|---|
| Aerobic power and capacity | Fartlek, 10-15 s, sprint – 3-6 min, work is at the anaerobic threshold level | Aerobic interval series |
| Anaerobic glycolitic power and capacity | Anaerobic power interval series | Anaerobic capacity interval series |
| Maximal speed | Anaerobic alactic interval series | Anaerobic alactic exercises, explosive strength exercises |
| Techno-tactical abilities | Techno-tactical simulation, maximum speed | Match |

An additional comment should be made with regard to sequencing of resistance workouts and game practice in dual and team sports. Regular strength training is an indispensable part of in-season preparation on professional and semi-professional teams. Extensive data indicate that a long playing season of 20-35 weeks may result in dramatic losses of lean body mass, and maximum and explosive strength

(Baker, 2001; Gamble, 2006). Thus, the necessity for combining high-resistance workouts with daily game practice is typical and generally approved. Very frequently game practices are planned for the afternoon hours (mostly because of organizational restrictions, professional or educational demands for some of the athletes, etc.). The question is whether the morning hours can be exploited for effective strength training because high-resistance training produces neuromuscular fatigue that may have a detrimental impact on techno-tactical game abilities during subsequent game practice. This important practical issue was thoroughly examined in a special study (Woolstenhulme et al., 2004)

**Case study.** Highly trained female basketball players aged 18-22 yr executed an experimental program on two separate days. On one day they performed a full-body morning resistance workout that included 7 exercises, 3-6 sets with load levels ranging from 5 to 12 RM. After six hours of rest they were tested in the vertical jump, the 30 second anaerobic Wingate bicycle test, and a 60-second shooting accuracy trial. On another day the same measurement program was completed but without the preceding resistance training. The statistical analysis didn't reveal any differences between the athletes' results on the experimental and control days. Thus, a high-resistance full-body workout of moderate intensity has no negative impact on the manifestation of sport-specific athletic abilities of trained basketball players after six hours of rest (Woolstenhulme et al., 2004).

It can be concluded that the one-day workout program, even an extremely important one, is part of a larger training unit (micro-, mesocycle). Its interaction with preceding and subsequent workloads is of particular importance both for planning and performance.

## 2.4 How to structure a workout

Based on the material presented in this chapter, the general approach to structuring each single workout seems very comprehensive. Nevertheless, some summation of the relevant information in the form of an algorithm may be helpful. Experienced coaches, who perform this work almost automatically, will be able to compare their approach with the formal prescription while young coaches and athletes should accept the basic standard, which can assist them in developing their own style (Table 2.14).

**Table 2.14**

**General algorithm for structuring a single workout**

| No | Operations | Remarks |
|----|------------|---------|
| 1. | Determination of main and additional targets and load level | Should be done for the entire microcycle with respect to each workout and their expected interactions |
| 2. | Selection of appropriate organizational form | The expected interactions between the athletes and possible partnerships should be taken into account |
| 3. | Compilation of the key-exercise (key-task) | This includes prescription of all relevant performance details (speed, movement rate, expected response etc.) |
| 4. | Selection of other exercises | All exercises should be checked with regard to their reciprocal compatibility |
| 5. | Selection of appropriate warm-up and cool-down variants | Both warm-up and cool-down can be modified according to workout specific demands |
| 6. | Inspection of available equipment and workout conditions | Monitoring means, training machines, accessories and as far as possible, weather conditions, should be checked |

It may not be necessary to prepare a full description of each workout with all the details mentioned in the table, but all details should be taken into account. It is highly recommended to familiarize the athletes with the upcoming workout plan. World famous swim coach and sport scientist James Counsilman (1968) used to write the workout content on a large blackboard in front of the swimming pool. It was his contention that this definitely increases motivation and affects the consciousness needed to perform heavy workloads. In general, coaches should be ready to explain to curious athletes why they selected certain combinations of exercises and not others.

**Summary**

Workouts often seem to be a trivial and simple component of the training system that require no special consideration or clarification. But, the Block Periodization approach emphasizes several aspects of workout structure that were ignored or insufficiently considered previously. For example, the proposed aim-load related classification offers a distinction among three different workout types: development, which provides the major training stimuli for progress, retention that is aimed at maintaining several abilities at the level attained, and restoration, which facilitates recovery after the preceding high-load sessions. The proposed five-point scale enables coaches to quantify workouts according to load in any sport, where one point indicates the minimal level and five points – extreme workloads. Based on the experience of prominent coaches the term "*key-workout*" was proposed and explained. It stresses the most important development workouts that are focused on the main training objective and help facilitate the key-function.

Warm-up and cool-down are considered indispensable structural elements of a workout. This chapter stressed the role of warm-up in metabolic and technical adjustment, mental readiness and prevention of injuries. Similarly, the cool-down was considered from the viewpoint of restoration and injury prevention. The basic part of the workout was described with regard to the main content element which was termed the *key-exercise or key-task*. The methodological, psycho-physiological and organizational aspects of the key-exercise are also presented.

Guidelines for putting together the workout are given with respect to sequencing and reciprocal compatibility of different exercises. Thus, exercises for maximum speed, explosive strength, acquisition of new technical skills, and exercises to improve the neural mechanisms of maximal strength (1-3 RM) require appropriate excitatory neural input and should be performed when athletes are not fatigued. Exercises for anaerobic glycolitic endurance and maximal oxygen uptake can be fulfilled by moderately fatigued athletes who can still sustain the desired metabolic level. Exercises for strength endurance and aerobic endurance demand sustained efforts despite accumulated fatigue and can therefore be continued till the end of the workout.

The important point is that the Block Periodization Concept assumes minimization of training modalities within a workout as follows: one dominant modality, a second one that is compatible with the main objective, and a third one to improve technique/tactics or provide restoration. Usually 65-70 % of all training time in the development workout should be devoted to one-two specific training

Each workout
1) Dominant Modality
2) Secondary that is complimentary w/ Main objective
3) Tertiary to ↑ technique/tactics or provide restoration

modalities. Compatible combinations of different training modalities within single workouts are presented. Special attention is given to the one day workout series that can embrace two-six sessions. Factors such as load sequencing, exercise compatibility and athlete restoration are taken into consideration. In addition, general guidelines on how to structure daily series of workouts are given together with the most typical compatible combinations of two sequenced workouts in a day.

**References for Chapter 2**

Baker, D. (2001). The effect of an in-season of concurrent training on the maintenance of maximal strength and power in professional and college-aged rugby league football players. *J Strength Cond Res*, 15 (2), 172-177.

Bangsbo, J., Krustrup, P., González-Alonso, J., and Saltin, B.( 2001). ATP production and efficiency of human skeletal muscle during intense exercise: effect of previous exercise. *American Journal of Physiology, Endocrinology and Metabolism*, 280:E956-964.

Bonen, A., Belcastro,A.N. (1976). Comparison of self-selected recovery methods on lactic acid removal rates. *Med Sci Sports*, 8:176-181.

Borg, G. (1973). Perceived exertion: A note of "history" and method. *Medicine and Science in Sports*, 5, 90-93.

Counsilman, J. (1968). *The science of swimming*. Englewood Cliffs, N.J.: Prentice-Hall, Inc.

Ekstrand, J., Gillquist, J., Moller, M. et al. (1983). Incidence of soccer injuries and their relation to training and team success. *American J Sports Med*, 11, 63-67.

Fox, E.L., and Mathews, D.K. (1981). Physiological basis of physical education and athletics. 3rd edition. Philadelphia: W.B. Saunders.

Gamble, P. (2006). Periodisation of training in team sports athletes. *Strength Cond J*, 28 (5), 56-66.

Hagberg, J.B., Hickson, R., McLane, J.A. et al. (1979). Disappearance of norepinephrine from the circulation following strenuous exercise. *J Appl Physiol*, 47:1311-1316.

Hartfield, F.C. (1985). There are not sore muscles: If yours are after working out, here's what you can do. *Sports Fitness*. 1(8), 38-43.

High, D., Howley E., Franks, D. (1989). The effects of static stretching and warm-up on prevention of delayed-onset muscle soreness. Res Quaterly, 60, 357-361.

Issurin, V. (2003). Aspekte der kurzfristigen Planung im Konzept der Blockstruktur des Trainings.*Leistungspor*t, 33, 41-44.

Jezova, D., Vigas, M., Tatar, P. et al.(1985). Plasma testosterone and catecholamine response to physical exercise of different intensities in men. *Eur J Appl Physiol*, 54, 62-68.

Juel, C., Bangsbo, J., Graham, T., and Saltin, B.( 1990). Lactate and potassium fluxes from human skeletal muscle during and after intense, dynamic knee extensor. *Acta Physiol Scand*, 140, 147-156.

Lydiard, A. and Gilmour, G. (2000). *Running with Lydiard.* Meyer & Meyer Sport.

Maglischo, E.W. (1992). *Swimming even faster.* Mountain View, CA: Mayfield Publisher Company.

McArdle,W.D., Katch,F., Katch,V. (1991). *Exercise physiology.* Philadelphia/ London: Lea & Febiger

Powers, S. and Howley, F.T. (1994). *Exercise physiology: thery and application to fitness and performance.* Dubuque, Iowa: Wm. C. Brown Company Publisher.

Moller, M.H., Oberg, B.E., Gildquist J. (1985). Stretching exercises and soccer: effect of stretching on range of motion in the lower extremity in connection with soccer training. *Int J Sports Med*, 6, 50-52.

Noakes, T. (1991). *Lore of running.* 3rd edition. Champaign, IL: Leisure Press.

Shrier, I.,Gossal,K. (2000). Myths and truths on stretching. Individualized recommendations for healthy muscles. Phys Sportmed, 28, 1-7.

Sejersted, O.M., Villestad, N.K., and Medbo, J.I. (1986). Muscle and electrolyte balance during and following exercise. *Acta Physiol Scand*, 128 (Suppl.556), 119-125.

Spreuwenberg, L.P.B., Kraemer, W.J., Spiering, B.A. et al., (2006). Influence of exercise order in a resistance-training exercise session. *J Strength Cond Res*, 20 (1), 141-144.

deVries, H.A. (1986). *Physiology of exercises for physical education and athletics.* 4th edition. Dubuque, Iowa: Wm. C. Brown Company Publisher.

Viru, A. (1995). *Adaptation in sports training.* Boca Raton, FL: CRC Press

Volkov, N. (1986). Biochemistry of sport. In: Menshikov V. and Volkov, N. (Eds.), Biochemistry. Moscow: Fizkultura i sport, p.267-381.

Woolstenhulme, M.T., Balley, B.K., and Alisen, P.E. (2004). Verical jump, anaerobic power, and shooting accuracy are not altered 6 hours after strength training in collegiate women basketball players. J Strength Cond Res, 18 (3), 422-425.

Yanilov-Eden, O. (2005). Gal Friedman – gold medalist. In: Lustig G. and Khlebovsky E. (Eds.). *Summarization, analysis and results of the 2004 Athens Olympic Games.* Nethanya: Elite Sport Department of Israel, p.245-254 (in Hebrew)

Yessis, M. (2006) *Sports: Is it All B.S.?* Terre Haute, IN: Equilibrium Books.

Zakas, A., Grammatikopoulou, M., Zakas, N. et al., (2006). The effect of active warm-up and stretching on the flexibility of adolescent soccer players. *J Sports Med Phys Fitness*, 46, 57-61.

Zatsiorsky, V.M.(1995). *Science and practice of strength training*. Champaign, IL: Human Kinetics.

# Chapter 3

Gennadi Touretski (Russia, Switzerland - center), and his athletes:
Alexander Popov (Russia--left), Five-time Olympic champion,
many times world champion in swimming and
Michael Klim (Australia--right), two-time Olympic champion,
many times world champion in swimming

# Chapter 3

# Microcycles, mesocycles
# and training stages

*[handwritten: Micro: 1 week]*
*[handwritten: Meso: 4 week]*
*[handwritten: → Generally]*

The microcycle is the shortest training cycle. It encompasses a number of workouts and lasts a number of days, most often one week. The mesocycle, a medium size training cycle, incorporates a number of microcycles. A number of mesocycles in a specific sequence and with purposeful interaction form a training stage that is usually <u>directed to competition</u>. This chapter presents and elucidates the basics, essentials and designs of the various training units.

## 3.1. Microcycles

*[handwritten: → 4 day cycle spread to Next week would make a 7-9 day Micro.]*

As stated above, the microcycle usually lasts one week. This uniformity has no physiological rationale but <u>rather is based on social life</u>; athletes combine training with education and professional activity, and their normal desire to spend weekends with family and friends. However, training camps make it possible to create shorter and longer microcycles. These possibilities are considered below. Our attention in this chapter is directed to the types and specifications, load variations, compatibility of adjacent workouts, and in particular, the content of various microcycles.

### 3.1.1. Types and specifications of microcycles

There are six types of training microcycles, characterized by specific purposes, load levels, particulars of workload design and duration (Table 3.1).

**Table 3.1**

**Purpose, load level and particulars of different microcycles**

*3 cycles in-season*

| Type | Purpose | Load level | Particulars | Duration |
|------|---------|-----------|-------------|----------|
| Adjustment | Initial adaptation to appropriate loads | Medium | Gradual increase in workload | 5-7 days |
| Loading | Fitness development | Substantial - high | The use of big and substantial workloads | 5-9 days |
| Impact | Fitness development using extreme training stimuli | Very high - extreme | Use and summation of extreme workloads | 4-7 days |
| Pre-competitive | Immediate preparation for competition | Medium | Tuning for forthcoming competition, using event-specific means | 5-7 days |
| Competitive | Participation in competition | High – very high | Sport and event-specific performance | 2-7 days |
| Restoration | Active recovery | Low | Use of a wide spectrum of restorative means | 3-7 days |

*1) 2) 3) 4) 5) ↓ Repeat*

As can be seen in Table 3.1 the microcycles differ in purpose, load level, design, particulars, and duration. For example, the adjustment microcycle at the beginning of the season usually lasts a whole week. In the middle of the season this microcycle can be planned at the beginning of a new stage or used to start a training camp. In both cases its duration can be shorter (3-5 days) and depends on the circumstances of preparation. Note that gradual increases in load level relate not only to physiological demands (i.e. magnitude of training stimuli) but also to the mental load component. This can be particularly important in the training camp, where athletes simultaneously receive new cognitive and emotional demands. Similarly, the restoration microcycle varies in duration depending on fatigue level and the demands of preparation. Usually in mid-season, the restoration microcycle after training camp and/or after competition lasts 3-4 days.

*Camp demands stresses many athlete on an*

→A sport like Football w/ Multiple competitions would require shorter cycles.

The loading microcycles encompass mostly routine work and usually last one week but, this duration is not firmly set. Load administration in this cycle is considered separately in the next section. The impact microcycle focuses on maximal loads and can last less than a week. Special requirements should be in place to supply restorative means that are necessary for such microcycles in order to fulfill their goals. Proper diet, nutritional supplements, hydrotherapy, massage, mental relaxation, etc. can be parts of the special restoration program.

A pre-competitive microcycle can be shorter or longer than a week. It normally has two purposes: to provide mental, physical and techno-tactical tuning for a forthcoming event, and to provide full (or sometimes partial) recovery of athletes after serious loads. Consequently, this microcyle is characterized by a remarkable load reduction. The competitive microcycle is exclusively sport-specific; this determines its content, particulars and duration which, in extreme cases, can be more than one week, as in multi-day road cycling competitions. For instance, the world famous cycling "Tour-de-France" lasts twenty three days including two days off. Thus, this competition embraces three successive microcycles. The sequencing of different microcycles is considered in 3.2.

### 3.1.2. Load variations within the microcycle (wave-shape design)

It is commonly known that the load level should be varied within a microcycle. The main factors determining load variations are load summation that causes fatigue accumulation, and restoration, which is affected by the use of reduced load level workouts and other means of restoration. Previous considerations of load variability have been based on general categories such as small, medium and high load levels (Martin,1980; Starischka, 1988) or in percentages of maximum (Dick,1980; Platonov,1997; Bompa,1999). Adequate and integrative load description is a problem, particularly for non-measurable sports like sailing or team and dual sports. The 5-point load level scale presented in the previous chapter (2.1.3) makes it possible to formalize workload alterations within several microcycles. For example see typical load variations in microcycles having one workout per day in Figure 3.1.

Three- and two-peak designs are used most widely because they allow athletes to perform relatively large amounts of weekly workloads with reduced risk of excessive fatigue accumulation. The two or three load reductions facilitate athletes' restoration and stimulate their readiness to effectively perform subsequent high demand workouts. The key-workouts concentrate the most important workloads of dominant training modalities.

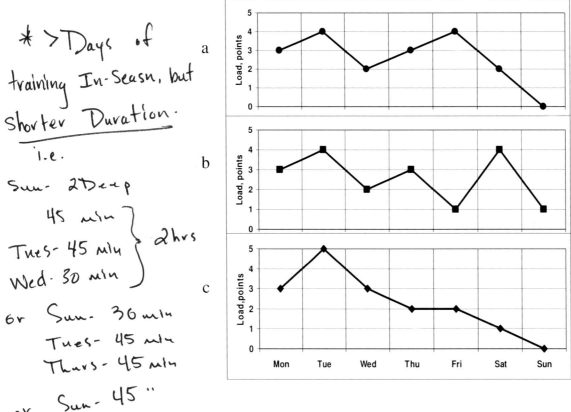

*Handwritten notes (left margin):*

\* >Days of training In-Seasn, but Shorter Duration.

i.e.

Sun- 2Deep
45 min
Tues- 45 min  } 2hrs
Wed- 30 min

or Sun- 36 min
Tues- 45 min
Thurs- 45 min

or Sun- 45 "
Wed- 45 "
Fri- 30 "

**Figure 3.1.** Two (a), three (b), and one-peak (c) load variations within a training microcycle

*Handwritten notes (left margin):*

↓  4-7-12
\*My Own training...
Since I like to do running + Conditioning.

The one-peak design can be employed to concentrate a number of developing workouts in order to attain a more profound and stressful training response. This result can be used as preparation for further medium- and low-level workouts in which several technical and/or tactical tasks can be accomplished with gradual recovery. Such concentration of one-peak development workouts can definitely be used by sufficiently prepared high-performance athletes but not by novice and less prepared athletes.   →One Peak: Hi Level Athletes

When athletes do two or more workouts per day, the daily point-score is raised by each workout making the weekly point-score much higher (Figure 3.2). The graph displays load variations within a microcycle, where each coordinate summarizes the load values of one or two single workouts for several days. The load value for each

*Handwritten:* 1 wk

single workout is based on a 5-point scale. The first peak is created by two successive development workouts followed by two medium load supporting workouts. This makes restoration possible prior to the second mini-block of workloads composed of three development sessions including two key-workouts. The last session on Saturday can be devoted to a time-trial or a match in team or dual sports, or in some other competitive simulation.

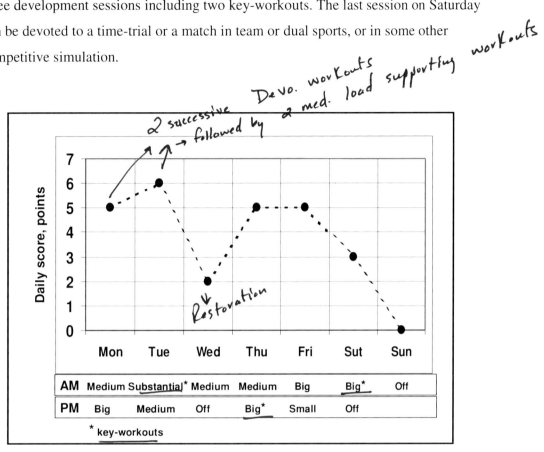

**Figure 3.2.** Two-peak load variation in a training microcycle with ten workouts
(Issurin, 2003)

Additional remarks can be made about a quantification system based on a 5-point scale. Its utilization offers a number of possible benefits.

First, the graphic presentation of the workload, particularly in non-measurable sports, gives additional support for coaches to analyze the load level of each workout and to quantify it more accurately. Also, different microcycles (one-, two- and, three-peak designs) can be expressed numerically and presented in visual form.

Second, the microcycle graph can be used didactically. Athletes can relate more consciously to training demands since they can better appreciate the importance of key-workouts and anticipate restoration after the stressed load peaks.

83

*✳*  Third, the total point-score of the whole microcycle can be used for general load evaluation and for comparing different microcycles. In this manner, planning technology can be enhanced.

As previously stated, the Block Periodization approach assumes a high concentration of specialized workloads directed at a minimum number of targeted abilities (1.3). This in turn determines the special demands of the appropriate microcycles, which should show mostly separate, not complex, distribution of workloads taking into account their reciprocal interactions and expected training residuals. *→ Separate Training Abilities.*

The next paragraphs consider the most widely used aerobic (or strength-aerobic) microcycle (3.1.3), anaerobic glycolitic microcycle (3.1.4), microcycle for explosive strength in highly coordinated exercises (3.1.5), and the pre-competitive microcycle (3.1.6).

### 3.1.3. Microcycle to develop aerobic (strength-aerobic) abilities.

*→ Tri, Duathlon, etc...*

Aerobic and so called strength-aerobic microcycles make up a large part of the overall general preparation in many sports. They develop the aerobic endurance and muscular strength that is needed for performance in all endurance, combat, team and dual sports, several aesthetic sports like synchronized swimming and figure skating, and others. Combined aerobic and strength exercises needs special clarification. On the one hand, this combination reduces strength increases in comparison to strength training alone (Zatsiorsky, 1985). On the other hand, strength training by itself increases muscle mass that has a relatively low oxidative capability (Wilmore & Costill, 1993 and others). Hence, enlarged muscle mass that is not supported by a proportional increase in aerobic enzymes and mitochondrial mass will not benefit athletic performance in many of the above mentioned sports. Of course, the proportion of aerobic and strength exercises within a microcycle can vary, depending on athletic demands and/or individual desires. Let's consider the particulars of the strength-aerobic microcycle of multi World and Olympic swimming champion Alexander Popov (Russia).

84

> **Example**. Alexander Popov, one of the greatest swimmers specializing in 50 and 100m Freestyle sprint events, has drawn a lot of attention to aerobic and strength workloads. Aerobic microcycles formed the essence of his training in the preparatorty phase, corresponding to the accumulation mesocycle in Block Periodization terms. Figure 3.3 displays the training modalities of exercises performed in ten full workouts. Popov's typical strength-aerobic microcycle highlights the large amount of exercises at the Anaerobic Threshold (AT) level and technical drills (Tech) directed at stroke perfection. These technical drills were performed while counting strokes and targeting a number of movement cycles for each speed regime which affected both technique and swim-specific strength effectively. Maximal Speed (MS) exercises (anaerobic alactic) were performed each day in medium proportions, while Aerobic Power (AP) exercises were done in only three workouts. Strength Endurance (SE) drills, i.e. aerobic speed resistance exercises, were another large contributor to the program. Anaerobic Glycolitic (AnG) exercises were employed once in the 200m time trial on the stepwise incremental all-out test (courtesy of Gennadi Touretski, personal communication).

The above example is evidence that:

a) even in the training of a prominent sprinter, the contribution of aerobic endurance exercises is very high;

b) strength abilities can be effectively developed by means of force accentuation in sport-specific drills and;

c) despite the high contribution of anaerobic glycolitic power and capacity in the metabolic profile of 100m Freestyle swimmers, the use of anaerobic glycolitic exercises in the strength-aerobic microcycle program is negligible. This last circumstance is particularly important in light of Block Periodization.

*Don't train Anaerobic Glycolysis that prominently.*

The athlete's body can not respond effectively to training stimuli that simultaneously affect very different physiological systems. Highly intense glycolitic workloads cause a profound metabolic response and hormonal shift that can last two-three days (Viru, 1995). Superimposed training responses beyond aerobic and glycolitic-anaerobic exercises leads to conflict in the adaptation process. Moreover, highly accentuated aerobic exercises are intended to create profound physiological changes like muscle capillarization, increased aerobic enzymes, myoglobin and mitochondrial volume. All of these changes take place during post-exercise recovery.

→ Trying to stimulate aerobic + anaerobic-glycolitic adaptations at the same time leads to less training effect.

The addition of anaerobic glycolitic workloads, however, leads to a disruption in metabolic adaptation and dramatically decreases the cumulative training effect.

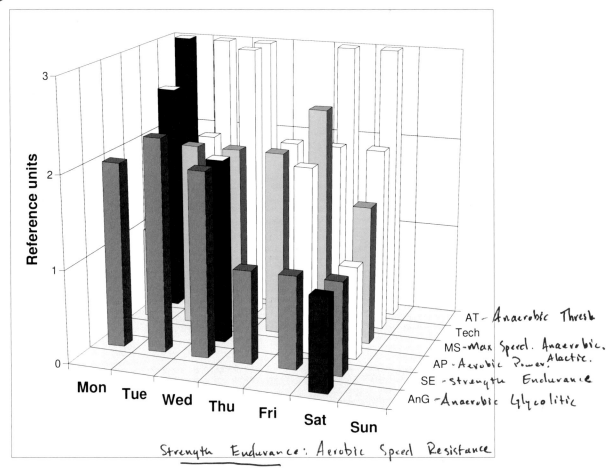

**Figure 3.3.** The sequencing of training modalities in the aerobic microcycle of multi Olympic champion Alexander Popov (courtesy of Gennadi Touretski, personal communication)

As previously stated, the Block Periodization approach postulates minimizing the number of targeted abilities within one mesocycle and consequently, in the microcycle as well. Compatible training modalities in the aerobic microcycle include: maximum strength (first priority), anaerobic alactic abilities (maximum speed), aerobic strength-endurance as a part of aerobic potential, and movement technique (Table 3.2).

## Table 3.2

### Aerobic microcycle with compatible training modalities in regard to training design and methodical background

| Training modality | Training design | Methodical background |
|---|---|---|
| Maximum strength | Strength workouts demand sufficient recovery time for anabolism | Combining aerobic and strength workouts ensures better oxidation in enlarged muscles |
| Anaerobic alactic (maximum speed) abilities | There are two options; 1) alternating exercises 2) including alactic sprint series | Sprints break monotony and activate a wide spectrum of muscle fibers that can be exploited in subsequent aerobic workloads |
| Aerobic strength endurance | Use of speed resisted exercises in appropriate metabolic regimes | Additional resistance (weight) stimulates force application in power phases of movement |
| Movement technique | Learning new skills; accentuation of technical details in performing drills | Perfection of technique doesn't aggravate metabolic adaptation to both aerobic and strength workloads |

In planning strength workouts in the aerobic microcycle, it is important to remember that its effectiveness depends on the testosterone/cortisol ratio that affects protein synthesis in skeletal muscles. After endurance workloads this ratio remains decreased for many hours, an unfavorable time for carrying out strength workouts (Viru, Karelson & Smirnova, 1992). On the other hand, high-resistance workouts increase the rate of protein turnover, which persists for at least 24 hours (Chesley et al., 1992). Therefore, developing workouts for maximal strength should not be performed in the shadow of the preceding exhaustive aerobic training. There must be 24 hours of recovery during which time only low-level loads can be managed.

Anaerobic alactic exercises do not have primary importance in the aerobic microcycle but their contribution is far from negligible. Sprints used in alternating exercises (like fartlek) recruit the fast motor units that are normally inactive in drills of moderate intensity (Komi, 1989). The short-term oxygen debt caused by the sprint should be compensated for during subsequent aerobic work. Thus additional stimuli for oxidation are received by both low and fast muscle fibers. A break in monotony and elevation of emotional intensity in the aerobic workout are also valuable contributions of sprint exercises.

*[handwritten margin notes:]* Test/Cortisol Ratio. ← Another reason to lift then run. → 24 hr of Low load after aerobic training. {Max Speed} → Aerobic Tri-Training

*[handwritten bottom notes:]* 11-24-13 Idea 1 — Day 1 Max ST – Day 2 Aerobic – Day 3 Low load Recover – Day 4 Max ST Max Sp. – Day 5 Aerobic – Day 6 Low Load Recover – Day 7 Max Spd

A large number of moderately intense exercises is needed to carry out many technical drills directed at enhancing basic technique details and elements. This includes features such as automatization, biomechanical economy, full range of motion, accentuation of force application and enhancement of relaxation and in power phases, effective variability following changed conditions, and fatigue tolerance all of which can be successfully affected during prolonged aerobic exercise.

The chart of a typical strength-aerobic microcycle (Figure 3.4) presents the general approach to training design taking into account the above mentioned demands of high-resistance workouts.

→ Why is Max Strength posted after Aerobic endurance on the same day?

| | | Mon | Tue | Wed | Thu | Fri | Sat | Sun |
|---|---|---|---|---|---|---|---|---|
| **1st workout** | Dominant training modality | AE | AE | MS | ALA | AE | MS | |
| | Secondary training modality | Tech | ALA | AE | AE | Tech | ALA | |
| | Load level | Subst | Subst | Big | Medium | Big | Subst | |
| **2nd workout** | Dominant training modality | MS | Rest | | AE | Rest | | |
| | Secondary training modality | ALA | Tech | | MS | Tech | | |
| | Load level | Medium | Low | | Subst | Low | | |

**Figure 3.4.** General presentation of aerobic microcycle consisting of ten workouts; ⬚ - key-workout; AE – aerobic endurance, MS – maximum strength, ALA – alactic abilities, Tech –technique perfection

### 3.1.4. Microcycle of high intensity anaerobic workloads.

*→ Must combine w/ compatible modalities.*

Microcycles of high intensity anaerobic workloads form the content of the most specific and exhaustive transmutation mesocycle. As already mentioned (1.2.3) the cumulative training effect of such training is highly dependent on the selection of compatible training modalities that make it possible to reinforce and produce the dominant workload effect (Table 3.3).

**Table 3.3**

**Anaerobic glycolitic microcycle--compatible training modalities with respect to training design and methodical background**

| Training modality | Training design | Methodical backgrounds |
|---|---|---|
| Strength endurance (mostly anaerobic) | High-resistance drills can be included in regular workouts or managed in separate sessions | High-resistance intense exercises produce a dual effect, development of strength endurance and enhance anaerobic metabolism |
| Anaerobic alactic (maximal speed) abilities | The favorable well-restored state usually can not be found; sprints can be used by moderately fatigued athletes | The alactic mechanism contributes to power output in short-duration bouts where the main target is maximal glycolitic power; sprints provide diversity and enrich training |
| Low intensity aerobic exercises | They are managed in each part of the workout and in separate sessions | Indispensable component of active restoration that also includes stretching, relaxation etc. |
| Movement technique | Combination of technical demands with dominant workloads; accentuation of the most meaningful technical details | Highly intense loads and fatigue accumulation suppress technical skills; specific measures are necessary to prevent these negative consequences |
| Tactics (focus on dual and team sports and combat sports) | The most stressful techno-tactical tasks get prime-time both in the session and microcycle | Combination of techno-tactical demands with physical strain elicit profound sport-specific training effects |

A few remarks must be made with regard to Table 3.3. First, the development workloads in this microcycle are performed at a load level higher than anaerobic threshold. Nevertheless, the extent of anaerobic resource mobilization may vary and depend on many factors. Normally the intensity level over the microcycle gradually increases as the target competition approaches. Hence, the utilization of workloads inducing lactate accumulation in the 5-8 mM range makes it possible to improve maximal aerobic power and aerobic-anaerobic interactions.  Such workouts can be prevalent in early- to mid-season. The workloads that elicit lactate accumulation over 8 mM are directed to enhancing anaerobic glycolitic power and capacity.  They contribute greatly in the final stages prior to the target-competition.

Second, high-resistance intensity exercises can comprise the main part of a training program. Typical drills such as uphill running, series jumping, resistance swimming, rowing, paddling, etc. activate the entire spectrum of muscle fibers. The recruitment of fast motor units leads to a rapid increase in lactate production and as a result, the extent of anaerobiosis in such workloads is relatively higher but the duration for sustaining the given load level is shorter. Thus, the intense strength endurance workout is an important contributor to the anaerobic microcycle of a training program. *Fast M.U. leads to Rapid ↑ Lactate production.*

Third, anaerobic alactic exercises are compatible with an anaerobic glycolitic program, with restrictions. They require proper metabolic, enzymatic and neural adjustment that can not be sufficiently provided for within an exhausting and strictly managed microcycle. However, the specific demands of several sports (in particular team and dual sports and combat sports) dictate involvement of short-duration bouts (alactic) and more prolonged efforts (glycolitic). In addition, the use of short-duration sprints makes it possible to diversify the training routine but without attempting to enhance maximal speed. *→ Can Sprint. but Not w/ Goal of getting faster*

Fourth, the metabolic stress typical of high intensity anaerobic exercises makes it more difficult to perform proper technique and techno-tactical skills. However, similar (or even more pronounced) aggravation occurs during competitive performance. Hence, these skills should be properly enhanced with respect to extreme physical and emotional exertions, i.e. within the framework of highly intense workload microcycles.

*Salient: Most notable or important*

As was stated and emphasized, the principal salient features of the anaerobic microcycle are fatigue accumulation and insufficient restoration. Indeed, Block Periodization postulates a high concentration of training on a reduced number of targeted abilities. Highly intense glycolitic workloads cause the most pronounced training reactions.] This occurs mainly in the cardiovascular system with attainment of maximal heart rate and cardiac output (Noakes, 2000), in energy supply with maximal oxygen deficit and debt and a maximal increase and accumulation of blood lactate (Saltin, 1986; Astrand et al., 2003). In addition, there is a rapid increase in adrenalin, noradrenalin and cortisol while testosterone levels decrease for a period of 24 or more hours (Viru, 1995). Taking into account workout frequency (6-12 per week) and post-exercise recovery duration, fatigue accumulation over an entire microcycle is → You will develop inevitable. To reduce the negative consequences of insufficient restoration the accum. fatigue. following guidelines are proposed:

a) the sequencing of development workouts should be thoroughly examined from the viewpoint of expected fatigue accumulation;

b) restoration workouts are a very important part of a training plan and should be distributed reasonably;

c) the inclusion of restoration entails appropriate exercises (stretching, relaxation, low intensity drills etc), massage, physiotherapy and nutritional supplements are strongly recommended;

d) monitoring the training response has particular importance here.

Based on the above and taking into account the optimal timing for different training modalities (Figure 3.3), many versions of the microcycle plan can be compiled. The general chart of an[anaerobic microcycle containing ten workouts is presented in Figure 3.5.]

Adrenaline (Epinephrine): Hormone + Neurotransmitter.
   - Regulates HR, Blood vessel and air passage diameters and metabolic shifts.
   - Fight-or-Flight of SNS.

NorAdrenaline: Catecholamine. ↑ in NorAdrenaline or NE as Neurotransmitter f/ Sympathetic Neurons in SNS ↑ contractions in Heart.

Cortisol: Steroid hormone. Released in response to stress + low blood gluccocorticoids. Primary Fxns: ↑ Blood sugar thru glycogenolysis; suppress immune system + aid in fat, protein + carb metabolism.

| | | Mon | Tue | Wed | Thu | Fri | Sat | Sun |
|---|---|---|---|---|---|---|---|---|
| **1st workout** | Dominant training modality | AGP | AGC | AGP | SE | ALA | AGC | |
| | Secondary training modality | Tech | ALA | SE | AGC | Tech | SE | |
| | Load level | Subst | Big | Subst | Big | Medium | Subst | |
| **2nd workout** | Dominant training modality | SE | Rest | | Rest | AGP | | |
| | Secondary training modality | ALA | Tech | | Tech | Tech | | |
| | Load level | Medium | Low | | Low | Big | | |

**Figure 3.5.** General presentation of a microcycle of highly intense anaerobic workloads; ALA – alactate abilities, AGP –anaerobic glycolitic power, AGC – anaerobic glycolitic capacity, SE – strength endurance, Rest – restoration.

A number of essential details must be mentioned with regard to the proposed design:

a)  A microcycle contains six development workouts directed at anaerobic glycolitic power and capacity and strength endurance with an anaerobic component.  Three key-workouts are focused on these three training modalities;

b)  The key-workouts are ensured by preceding them with medium load sessions or a restoration "window" on Wednesday evening.  Subsequent restorative workouts are intended to prevent excessive fatigue accumulation until the microcycle ends;

c)  Anaerobic alactic abilities are stressed in two medium load workouts intended to maintain the upper limit of speed.  Both restoration workouts are structured with low intensity drills that are also intended to support or enhance the sport-specific technical skills;

d)  It should be noted that load variation in the chart corresponds to a three-peak design.  Most likely two- and three-peak variations are best suited for high intensity anaerobic workload microcycles.

### 3.1.5. Microcycle for explosive strength in highly coordinated exercises.

Unlike so called metabolic sports, where energy production plays a decisive role in athletic performance, highly coordinated power sports have very specific demands in regard to fatigue accumulation. The neuro-muscular specificity of these sports and the salient manifestations of explosive strength, assume a suitable background for development workouts and, consequently, for high workload microcycles. This includes sufficient sensitivity and reactivity of the central nervous system (Zatsiorsky, 1995), rapid replenishment of energy resources (Wilmore, Costill, 1993), and an appropriate hormonal state, i.e., a beneficial testosterone/cortisol ratio (Viru, 1995). Therefore, a microcycle of highly specific workloads that is typical for the transmutation mesocycle, substantially differs from the equivalent microcycle in endurance sports. The typical disciplines in the power sports category are the throws (discus, javelin, hammer, shot put) and jumps (high, long, triple and pole vault). Let's consider the typical microcycle for developing explosive strength in a highly coordinated discipline using the hammer throw as an example.

*HAMMER EXAMPLE*

---

**Example**. The microcycle under consideration is taken from the preparation of two-time Olympic champion and Olympic silver medal winner for the hammer throw Yuri Sedykh (USSR). The microcycle contains a total of eleven workouts in which all development sessions are directed exclusively to explosive strength, event-specific technique and maximal strength. The content of the microcycle was reported by the athlete's personal coach (Bondarchuk, 1986). See Table 3.4.

---

A study of this microcycle reveals a number of essential details that can be considered characteristic of this type of training:

a) Event-specific explosive strength exercises, which are of primary importance, are placed exclusively in morning sessions and always in the initial part of the workout. This approach assures the most favorable phases of the athlete's physical state for performing the most important key-exercises;

b) The maximum strength exercises, which play an important supporting role in event-specific power and the athlete's conditioning, were employed in five sessions: four times separately in special evening workouts and once in the second part of the morning session;

93

c) Additional explosive strength exercises (standing jumps) were performed three times but not when the athlete was in his best condition;

d) Restorative exercises (playing basketball, swimming, stretching) were organically involved in the training program and even the day off included a recovery session.

**Table 3.4**

**Microcycle of highly specific workloads in the preparation of Olympic champion Yuri Sedyhk for the hammer throw (Bondarchuk, 1986)**

| Day | A.M. | | P.M. | |
|-----|------|--|------|--|
| | Content | Training modality | Content | Training modality |
| Mon | Throwing different weight hammers, 30 throws; Standing long jumps | ExpS + Tech<br><br>ExpS | Sprint runs of 5-20m Barbell exercises---snatch, half squats, good mornings Stretching | ALA MS |
| Tue | Throwing different weight hammers, 30 throws | ExpS + Tech | Barbell exercises---rotary torso, half squats Standing jumps | MS<br><br>ExpS |
| Wed | Throwing 16 kg weight, 25 throws; throwing the shot using different techniques, 50 throws. Playing basketball – 15 min | ExpS<br><br><br><br>Rest | Off | |
| Thu | Throwing of different weight hammers, 35 throws Barbell---snatch, half squats, good mornings, rotary torso. Swimming pool – 25 min | ExpS + Tech<br><br>MS<br><br>Rest | Off | |
| Fri | Throwing different weight hammers, 32 throws Standing jumps. | ExpS + Tech<br><br>ExpS | Barbell---snatch, half squats, good morning, rotary torso. Stretching. | MS<br><br>Rest |
| Sat | Throwing the 16 kg weight, 25 throws | ExpS | Barbell---snatch, half squats, good morning, rotary torso. Stretching. Playing basketball – 20 min | MS<br><br>Rest |
| Sun | Walking; swimming pool – 30 min | Rest | Off | |

**Key**: Exp S – explosive strength, Tech – technical (technique), MS – maximum strength

Based on the training program in this table, it is possible to reconstruct the typical microcycle for developing explosive strength in a highly coordinated throwing discipline (Figure 3.6). [The key factor in creating or using specialized exercises for development of special strength or explosive strength in highly coordinated sports events is that the coach understand technique of the skill and then couple it with the exercise.] In other words, the strength or explosive exercise duplicates (simulates) the technique so that both technique and strength are improved simultaneously as used in competition (Yessis, 2006).

| | | Mon | Tue | Wed | Thu | Fri | Sat | Sun |
|---|---|---|---|---|---|---|---|---|
| **1st workout** | Dominant training modality | ExpS | ExpS | ExpS | ExpS | ExpS | ExpS | Rest |
| | Secondary training modality | Tech | Tech | Rest | MS | Tech | MS | |
| | Load level | Subst | Subst | Subst | Big | Subst | Big | Low |
| **2nd workout** | Dominant training modality | MS | MS | | | MS | MS | |
| | Secondary training modality | ALA | ExpS | | | Rest | Rest | |
| | Load level | Medium | Medium | | | Medium | Medium | |

**Figure 3.6.** General presentation of a microcycle for developing explosive strength in a highly coordinated throws event based on a typical microcycle of Yuri Sedykh – Olympic hammer throw champion

Key, same as Table 3.4.

It is worth noting that the corresponding microcycle in the jump events has many specific features like sprint exercises, etc. Nevertheless, the above mentioned particulars (Figure 3.6) remain relevant for other explosive strength disciplines.

When considering microcycle design in explosive strength (power) sports, [special attention should be given to the suppressive impact of excessive fatigue accumulation.] This detrimental effect appears most particularly in the neural and hormonal spheres among athletes. It is well known that explosive strength depends on sensitivity and reactivity of the neuro-muscular system and that excessive fatigue disrupts the subtle regulation of neural input and muscle contraction. The hormonal effect also plays a decisive role in training responses to explosive strength sessions. Testosterone as the primary male sex hormone, determines the anabolic effect of strength training. In addition, its variations during athletic training indicate the level of induced physical stress (Viru and Viru, 2000). For example, the influence of testosterone on explosive performance was examined in a special study (Cardinale and Stone, 2006)

> **Case study**. Seventy elite athletes in track and field (sprinters), handball, volleyball and soccer players (a total of 22 women and 48 men) participated. Resting testosterone levels in blood and height of a countermovement vertical jump were examined after 10 hours of fasting and one day of rest. A significant positive relationship was found between testosterone levels and jump performance ($r = 0.61$, $p < 0.001$). Thus, testosterone levels strongly affect power output in muscular efforts having short contraction times (Cardinale and Stone, 2006).

The study findings lead to at least two conclusions for explosive strength training:

1)  persons with relatively high testosterone levels (both male and female athletes) have an inherited predisposition for explosive strength performance;

2)  the training design in microcycles for explosive strength development should avoid excessive fatigue that suppresses the testosterone level and sharply reduces the effect of maximal power exercises. *This is why... at least I assume that Peak Speed was designed that way.*

### 3.1.6. Pre-competitive microcycle

The pre-competitive microcycle forms the content of the realization mesocycle (1.2.2) and should satisfy the following demands:

a)  That it have sport-specific exercises and tasks that simulate forthcoming competitive activity and it develops mental readiness and toughness;

b)  That it develops maximal speed (power) abilities and sport-specific quickness;

c)  That it offers full restoration after highly fatiguing workloads in the preceding transmutation mesocycle.

96

There is one more demand that relates to mental readiness for forthcoming competition. Its importance increases as the competition approaches, although mental preparation is incorporated into the training process at earlier stages as well.

Because the pre-competitive microcycle is part of the realization mesocycle, also called the taper, its methodological clarification and interpretation is quite different. Basically, it is intended to reduce the total workloads but the ways of attaining this goal vary. It is generally believed that total training volume should be decreased but many contradictions exist regarding workout duration and frequency of high intensity exercises (Kubukeli et al., 2002). The Block Periodization concept makes it possible to propose general approaches that can assist in designing the pre-competitive microcycle in several sports (Table 3.5).

**Table 3.5**

**The major characteristics and particulars of pre-competitive microcycles**

| Major characteristics | Particulars | Comments |
|---|---|---|
| Workload volume | Substantially reduced | This creates conditions for full recovery |
| Total volume of intense exercises | Substantially reduced in comparison to the previous mesocycle | Total volume of drills decreases to facilitate recovery but the quality increases |
| Contribution of maximum speed (power) exercises | Substantially increased | Well rested athletes respond better to maximal speed drills; training residuals of maximal speed training are the shortest. |
| Contribution of sport-specific tasks | Substantially increased | These simulative tasks allow better adaptation to expected competitive stressors |
| Workout frequency | Usually similar to previous mesocycle | Subdivision of entire work into several portions allows for an increase in workout quality |
| Organization | Rational combination of group, individual and mixed workouts | This should be done with respect to sport-specificity and athlete individuality |
| Restoration | Beneficial conditions for full recovery; increased volume of restorative exercises/workouts | Athletes usually get more time and have greater desire to perform restorative exercises |

*[handwritten margin note:] →Max Speed adaptations Don't last long.*

*[handwritten margin note:] ↓ Vol but maintain freq.; ↑ Quality!*

Reduction of workload volume is a principal condition for full restoration in order to attain and then exploit, the state of supercompensation. In other words, reduction of the workload level is of primary importance but how it is done is based on different circumstances. The main factors in workload decrease are (1) a reduction in total training volume and (2) a reduction in partial volume of the intense exercises. The proportions are sport-specific and depend on the individual, but the outcome is always similar – restoration and improvement of the athlete's general state. This improved condition forms the background for the successful employment of two groups of exercises:

- maximal speed drills (recall that their effect depends on the reactivity of the central nervous system and the availability of energy resources), and
- sport-specific tasks simulating forthcoming techno-tactical competitive situations (well restored athletes can better approach model competitive regimes and adjust better to expected stressors).

Workout frequency, as a component of microcycle design, is neither simple nor unequivocal. On the one hand, reduced frequency can be considered as a way to decrease total workloads and to find more time for restoration. On the other hand, the division of daily workloads into two sessions makes it possible to increase the quality of highly intense exercises. Additional free time, particularly in the pre-competitive training camp, can be a serious disadvantage to the daily program. Thus, the preferred solution is to maintain the usual daily schedule for these athletes. In qualified athletes, particularly during the pre-competitive training camp, this means performing eight-ten workouts per week.

Workout organization in the pre-competitive microcycle is strongly dependent on the specificity of the sport and individual characteristics of the athletes. Of course, in team sports and team events such as rhythmic gymnastics or events in rowing and canoeing, group workouts are dominant. Nevertheless, the general tendency is toward a relative increase in individual workouts, where athletes can better concentrate on personal technical details, feelings, responses and proper ways of self-regulation. Also, proper contact with the coach affects the athletes' self-confidence.

The restorative workouts contribute more in this training plan than in other microcycles. This is explained, first of all, by the importance of the restorative process in the entire taper program and in attaining the supercompensation state for the competition period. In addition, because the time allocation is more liberal in the pre-competitive microcycle, there is better exploitation of restorative workouts and the use of exercises as tools to increase the quality of the most important sport-specific sessions.

Special attention should be given to the proper timing of workouts with regard to the expected schedule of competitions. In general, the daily biological rhythms should be adjusted to the schedule of the forthcoming competition, i.e., the most important workouts should be planned for the time of competitive peak-performance.

> **Example**. The canoe-kayak and rowing regatta programs at the Olympic Games from 1984-2004 were scheduled exclusively for the morning hours. This is in contrast to the program of world and continental championships in which races are held both in the morning and afternoon hours. Consequently, pre-Olympic preparation of world-class rowers and paddlers is planned in keeping with the expected time of maximal effort. This is especially typical of pre-competitive microcycles, where athletes perform sport specific simulative exercises in time for the forthcoming events.

The general chart of the pre-competitive microcycle presented here was compiled for training camp conditions and for expected competitive peak-performance times in the morning hours (Figure 3.7).

|  |  | Mon | Tue | Wed | Thu | Fri | Sat | Sun |
|---|---|---|---|---|---|---|---|---|
| **A.M.** | Dominant training modality | ALA | SSS | SSS | SSS | ALA | SSS | Rest |
| | Secondary training modality | Tech | Tech | MS | ALA | Tech | MS | |
| | Load level | Subst | Subst or big | Subst | Subst | Subst | Subst or big | Low |
| **P.M.** | Dominant training modality | MS or ExpS | Rest | | MS or ExpS | | Rest | |
| | Secondary training modality | Rest | ALA | | Rest | | ALA | |
| | Load level | Medium | Low | | Medium | | Low | |

**Figure 3.7.** General presentation of a pre-competitive microcycle oriented to peak-performance in the morning hours;

Key: SSS – sport-specific simulation task; ALA – alactate; Tech – technical; MS – maximum strength; ExpS – Explosive strength

It is worth noting the particular role of strength exercises in the design of pre-competitive microcycles. On the one hand, many athletes report that high-resistance exercises prior to competition negatively affect fine technical skills and the number of such exercises should be diminished or even excluded. This stance is especially typical among swimmers (Platonov, Fesenko, 1990) but also appears among volleyball and tennis players. On the other hand, the use of sport-specific exercises for maximal or/and explosive strength allows athletes to maintain the technical force component at the desired level (Bompa, Carrera, 2003). In addition, proper exercises for muscular hypertrophy prevent the uncontrolled reduction of muscle mass induced by stress hormones prior to and during competition.

### 3.1.7. Microcycle for sport-specific fitness maintenance in dual and team sports.

In-season preparation of high-performance team and dual sport athletes has very specific demands when applying the BP approach to training design. The sports season in soccer, American football, rugby, volleyball, etc. lasts 20-35

FB: Maintain Pre-Season ST 14-16 wks.

weeks where the possibility of inserting highly concentrated training blocks is very limited. In the typical situation, players maintain their strength abilities near pre-season levels for 14-16 weeks; afterwards, strength variables decrease dramatically (Fleck and Kraemer, 1997). The normal time span between the games (one week) doesn't allow effective work on the many disparate training targets such as metabolic conditioning, maximal and explosive strength, injury prevention, techno-tactical skills, game-specific endurance and active restoration. Thus, training priorities should be strictly determined and based on them, several approaches of BP can be incorporated:

- high concentration of specialized workloads within mini-blocks;
- separation of mini-blocks directed at different training modalities;
- determination of key-workouts.

The diagram in Figure 3.8 presents the proposed microcycle design.

1st Block-Mini / 2nd Mini Block

| | | Mon | Tue | Wed | Thu | Fri | Sat | Sun |
|---|---|---|---|---|---|---|---|---|
| A.M. | Dominant training modality | AR | MS | MS | | | TP | |
| | Secondary training modality | Cond | ExpS | ExpS | | | Tech | |
| | Load level | Medium or low | Subst | Big | | | Medium | Game |
| P.M. | Dominant training modality | | TP | AR | TP | | | |
| | Secondary training modality | | ExpS | Cond | Tech | | | |
| | Load level | | Medium | Low or medium | Subst or big | | | |

**Figure 3.8.** General presentation of a microcycle to maintain sport-specific fitness during in-season preparation in team and dual sports:

Key: AR – active recovery, TP – team practice, Cond – general conditioning Tech – technical; MS – maximum strength; ExpS – Explosive strength (the microcycle content of is based on Baker, 2001).

In the microcycle chart in Figure 3.8, the following particulars are worth noting:

1) The 1$^{st}$ mini-block (Monday- Wednesday) is devoted to mainly development of sport-specific strength abilities, i.e., maximal and explosive strength as the dominant training target. The mini-block begins with a workout for active recovery using medium or low load levels of aerobic and general conditioning exercises. The dominant target should be achieved in two key-workouts, which are combined with medium load level team practice (Tuesday afternoon) and a conditioning restorative workout (Wednesday afternoon). Thus, strength exercises as the important component of key-workouts, are followed by 28-30 hours of recovery that facilitates the anabolic process and restoration prior to the 2$^{nd}$ mini-block.

*[handwritten note in left margin: "Dominant target in 2. Key workouts."]*

2) The 2$^{nd}$ mini-block (Thursday- Saturday) targets sport-specific team practice and immediate preparation for the forthcoming game. It includes two obligatory team-practices. One of them precedes the day off and is intended to produce a pronounced game-specific training stimulus. The second workout immediately precedes the game, but with a restricted load level. Its content is usually connected with the expected particulars of the forthcoming match and as such, contains mostly techno-tactical drills.

Several highly motivated players and teams perform the in-season training microcycle without a day off. In this case the optional conditioning or techno-tactical workout can be executed on Friday morning (this optional session is not indicated on the figure). The possible merits of such planning are obvious. They facilitate the perfection of individual and/or collective techno-tactical skills and maintain the general conditioning level. The negatives of such a microcycle design are obvious as well – usually the players demand an entire day for their personal needs and mental recovery.

*[handwritten note in left margin: "Primary Target. Max strength."]*

3) The microcycle chart presented above gives priority to maximal strength development whereas explosive-type performances belong to the secondary target. Such an emphasis on a maximum strength program is based on the need for maintaining a favorable somatic, functional and anabolic status. Nevertheless there are examples of sequencing classic high-resistance training

with microcycles of ballistic explosive-type exercises that help to enhance jump performance (Newton et al., 2006).

The short time span and the emotional and physical stress associated with weekly competition, restrict the benefits of utilizing BP mesocycle sequencing. However, the benefits of accentuating dominant training targets, in a mini-block structure, and designing key-workouts can be attained despite variations in sports and local conditions.

### 3.1.8. How to construct a microcycle

The Block Periodization approach entails several specific considerations concerning microcycle construction. They relate to the function and importance of key-workouts. This includes: determination and compilation of key-workouts, facilitation of workload performance in key-workouts, monitoring the training etc. The restorative process also takes on greater importance because of the preparation involved in highly concentrated workloads and restoration after their execution. In general, the entire process of microcycle construction can be presented in a sequence of specific operations (Table 3.6).

**Table 3.6**

**The sequence of operations for compiling the training microcycle**

| N | Operation | Remarks |
|---|-----------|---------|
| 1 | Determination of dominant and secondary training modalities | This should be based on the annual plan and specificity of the current mesocycle |
| 2 | Determination, placement and compilation of key-workouts | These workouts should provide the main development impact of the training |
| 3 | Determination of restorative workouts and restorative "windows" | These measures facilitate performance of key-workouts and prevent excessive fatigue accumulation |
| 4 | Determination, placement and compilation of other developmental and supportive workouts | Workload interaction deserves special attention; preceding workouts affect sensitivity to subsequent workloads |
| 5 | Selection of appropriate means for monitoring training and for follow-up | Targeted abilities and functions are the focus of monitoring |
| 6 | Planning special events | This can involve a psychologist, physician, etc. or a special meeting, etc. |

In addition to the above schematic, a number of general rules can be proposed to facilitate microcycle training design.

The first rule – priority of key-workouts. The content and training modality of the key-workouts determine the main effect and direction of the whole microcycle. Thus, when the targeted abilities of a microcycle are clearly defined, the training design should start by structuring the key-workouts.

The second rule – arrangement of key-workouts. When structuring the sessions adjacent to key-workouts, their interaction should be taken into account. The preceding workout affects the athlete's sensitivity to developing workloads while the subsequent session determines fatigue accumulation and the restorative process.

The third rule – sharing restorative means. The restorative means, i.e., restorative workouts, restorative exercises (low intensity aerobic exercises, stretching, relaxation, shaking, breathing exercises), and restorative procedures (massage, sauna, hydro- and physiotherapy, mental training) form an indispensable component of training design. These means should be expertly planned in the framework of each microcycle.

*1st session of Microcycle should not be Key workout

The fourth rule - workload initiation and workload peaks. Usually a day-off decreases the athletes readiness for high workloads. Thus, the first session of the microcylcle should not be a key-workout. The number and placement of the key-workouts determine where the peak occurs and how many there are in the microcycle, i.e., one-peak, two-peak and three-peak designs.

The fifth rule – monitoring the training. The data from key-workout execution provide the best indication of the athletes' current state. This includes his current achievements, technical variables being performed at the required level, his responses, i.e., heart rate, blood lactate concentration, rate of perceived exertion, etc.

104

## 3.2. Mesocycles

The Block Periodization concept proposes three types of mesocycles (Table 1.7). As explained in Chapter 1, their general assessment and interpretation differ considerably from traditional training theory. Indeed, mesocycle-blocks form the essence of this alternative approach. They encompass both the extensive experience of prominent coaches in different sports and new concepts that clarify modern training. Thus, accumulation, transmutation and realization mesocycles will be considered in light of Block Periodization.

### 3.2.1. Accumulation mesocycle

In comparison to other mesocycles, this type is characterized by relatively high volumes of workloads at relatively reduced intensity. As the accumulation mesocycle is intended to develop basic athletic abilities, its duration, content and monitoring are of particular interest.

**Duration**. In general, two major factors impact the length of this mesocycle:
- sufficient time to attain the desired cumulative training effect in the targeted motor abilities;
- the time limitation dictated by the competitive calendar.

It has already been noted that the basic motor abilities developed in the majority of sports are aerobic endurance and maximal muscle strength. Progress in both of these abilities demands profound morphological and even organic changes. Therefore, sufficient time is needed for the physiological adaptation to take place. However, among qualified athletes having high levels of general fitness, relatively short periods of accentuated workloads provide substantial improvement in these abilities. Thus, it is important to determine the optimal duration for the mesocycle-block that will be sufficient to attain the desired changes but not excessively long so that the next mesocycle can start on time. This can be illustrated by the outcomes of a relevant case study.

105

**Case study**. Eight highly qualified female kayakers were monitored during a twenty week training program aimed at improving maximal strength abilities and aerobic endurance. High-resistance training lasted 4-5 hr/week; monitored by the measurement of maximal isometric force in kayak-specific body positions. The gain in maximal strength and the improvement rate differed greatly at the beginning, middle and end of the program (Figure 3.9). The initial three weeks induced average strength increases equal to 5.9%, i.e., an improvement rate of 1.93% per week; the next three weeks showed additional improvement of 1.6% and an improvement rate of 0.53%. Continuation of the program had a very modest impact, where the improvement rate decreased to 0.25 and 0.13% per week. Therefore, the entire fitness program was very effective at the beginning, reasonably effective through the first six weeks and had only a minor effect for the next 14 weeks (based on Sharobajko, 1984).

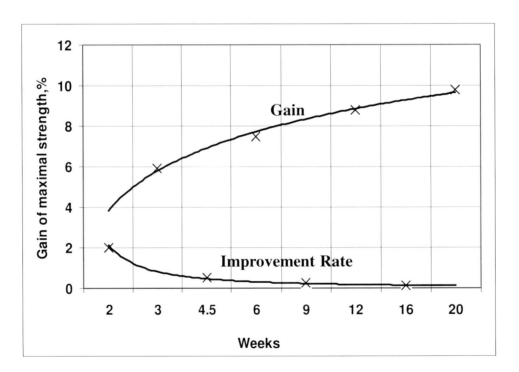

**Figure 3.9.** Gain in maximum strength and its improvement rate during a twenty week fitness program for highly qualified female kayakers (based on Sharobajko, 1984)

Similar trends have been noted during prolonged programs to improve aerobic endurance. This corresponds to the general biological concept that the adaptive → *Diminished Returns.* response induced by long-term training declines with time (Bouchard, 1986). All of the above further supports the general idea underlying Block Periodization--that training should be divided into shorter periods and use higher improvement rates for developing different abilities.

The cumulative training effect is characterized not only by gains in specific motor abilities but also by profound changes in physiological systems. This is particularly relevant in early season preparation when enhancement of basic abilities and functions is of special importance. Therefore, the accumulation mesocycle can be longer (up to six weeks) when training is intended to elicit more profound physiological changes, or shorter (three weeks or less) when training is intended to stimulate basic abilities and refresh general responses.

The time limits imposed by the competition calendar have a strong impact on mesocycle planning. Early in the season, athletes are usually less dependent on competition scheduling. In such cases the mesocycle duration can be based exclusively on coaching concepts. At mid-season, the timing of important competitions dictates the sequence and duration of training stages. Consequently, the accumulation mesocycle can be shortened to three-four weeks while at the end of the season, important competitions can come at relatively short intervals and the length of the accumulation mesocycle can be reduced to 10-14 days.

**Content.** The selection and sequence of appropriate microcycles substantially determine mesocycle content in terms of load variation (Table 3.7).

**Table 3.7**

**Selection and sequence of different microcycles (McC) when structuring an accumulation mesocycle**

| Part of mesocycle | Content (types of McC) | Comments |
|---|---|---|
| Initial | Restoration | This McC is suited to initiating a new training stage; not necessary after transition period |
| | Adjustment | This McC continues the initial part and can be shorter than a week |
| Mid- and end parts | Loading | The number of these McC determines the total duration of the whole mesocycle |
| Options | Impact | Can be administered in the mid-part with the duration about 3-6 days |
| | Restoration | Can be planned immediately after impact McC and followed by a loading McC |

In general, the load level should be gradually increased in the initial part of the mesocycle and the maximal load level should be achieved and maintained in the mid part. However, at the end, it is better to reduce the load level in order to start the next mesocycle without excessive fatigue. In special cases, the restorative microcycle (usually lasting three-four days) can be inserted towards the end of the accumulation block in order to start the next transmutation mesocycle in good condition.

**Monitoring the training**. The main purpose of monitoring is to assess the planned workloads and to evaluate current changes in targeted abilities and the athletes' training responses. The general approach to implementing the monitoring is presented in Table 3.8

**Table 3.8**

**Major characteristics and indicators for monitoring the training in the**

**accumulation mesocycle**

| Major characteristics | Indicators | Comments |
|---|---|---|
| Workload performance | Total mileage per week<br>Total number of sport-specific repetitions per week<br>Outcomes of key-workouts | The following should be analyzed:<br>- actual vs. planned;<br>- week to week trends<br>- trends within season |
| Targeted (basic) abilities | Results in time-trials<br>Results in free weight trials<br>Average results in key-workouts | It is suggested that appropriate valid tests be used |
| Training responses | Resting Heart Rate<br>Blood urea and CPK<br>Body mass, muscle mass<br>Fat component<br>Blood lactate after trials and exercises of special interest | The follow up is aimed to reveal the following:<br>a) that the level of fatigue is reasonable,<br>b) that the athletes attain the desired changes in their condition |

With regard to Block Periodization, the importance of developmental and particularly key-workouts, should once again be emphasized. Comparison of key-workouts performed in successive microcycles can be done with respect to exercise volume (mileage, repetitions, sum of the lifted weight, etc.), performance results (average time of series, average movement rate), and measurable training responses (HR, blood lactate etc.).

In addition, the strength training that affects muscle hypertrophy causes an increase in muscle mass and perhaps body weight as well. However, the accentuated aerobic endurance training can reduce the fat component. Therefore, athletes' anthropometric changes can be measurable outcomes when evaluating mesocycle training. In sports where changes in body mass are undesirable (i.e. gymnastics or sports with weight categories) this information is of special interest and draws much attention. Such changes should be carefully monitored in order to provide the coach and athletes with valuable information.

### 3.2.2. Transmutation mesocycle

According to Block Periodization, the transmutation mesocycle contains the most stressful sport-specific workloads. The general idea behind this mesocycle is to transmute the accumulated basic abilities into specific physical and techno-tactical fitness. As compared with other types, this mesocycle is characterized by the following:

a) The targeted abilities are more specialized; the key-exercises are tightly connected with competitive activity;

b) The intensity of developmental workloads is relatively higher and the volume of exercises with increased intensity is higher as well;

c) This is the most fatiguing mesocycle. Consequently, use of restorative means and stress monitoring are of paramount importance.

These features of the transmutation mesocycle determine its duration and content as well as the particulars for monitoring the training.

**Duration** of this type mesocycle is determined by various factors, summarized in Table 3.9.

**Table 3.9**

**Factors influencing duration of the transmutation mesocycle**

| Factors | Impact | Comments |
|---|---|---|
| Limitations caused by accumulation of fatigue | Fatigue, produced by highly concentrated intense workloads, approaches the upper limits in 3-4 weeks | Excessive fatigue can be obviated by inclusion of a restorative microcycle or an aerobic mini-block |
| Duration of the residual training effect caused by the previous mesocycle | After 4 weeks of highly intense workloads, the effect of the previous aerobic mesocycle drops dramatically | The residual training effect of the preceding mesocycle decreases with time and markedly after one month (Table 1.6) |
| Limitations created by the competition calendar | A short time period between important events requires a shortening of the mesocycle | In this case, mesocycle duration depends on calendar restrictions |

As can be seen in Table 3.9, the transmutation mesocycle, as a training block of highly specialized intense workloads, usually lasts no more than four weeks. The dominant factors limiting its duration differ, depending on the proximity of important competitions.  In early season, duration is affected most by accumulation of fatigue, while at end-season, mesocycle duration is determined by the calendar of important events.  In mid-season both of these factors affect duration in varying proportions.

The duration of training residuals induced by the previous accumulation mesocycle has a rather complicated, complex influence. On the one hand, basic motor ability (aerobic endurance, maximal muscle strength) decreases and approaches the critical level over four weeks. Consequently, if the transmutation mesocycle and subsequent realization mesocycle last six weeks the athletes will come to competition with attenuated aerobic and strength potential. On the other hand, many sports events require that a large amount of anaerobic glycolitic workloads be managed over a more prolonged period. This methodic contradiction can be surmounted by including a short-term aerobic mini-block within a prolonged anaerobic mesocycle (see 3.3.3).

**Content** of the transmutation mesocycle is formed by a number of sequenced microcycles, which are characterized in Table 3.10.

**Table 3.10**

**Selection and sequence of different microcycles (McC) to structure a transmutation mesocycle**

| Part of mesocycle | Content (type of McC offered) | Comments |
|---|---|---|
| Initial | Loading | The load level gradually increases during the initial McC (usually one week) |
| Mid- and ending part | Loading and/or Impact | The Impact McC can last less than a week (3-4 days) |
| Options | Competition (trial) | Participation in competition when fatigued is not excluded |
| | Restoration | This McC can be inserted after the impact McC and followed by a loading McC |
| | Aerobic contrast mini-block | This McC (2-4 days) can be included to prolong the aerobic training residuals |

As can be seen from Table 3.10, the transmutation mesocycle is made up mostly of loading microcycles and the impact microcycle can be moderate as well. Inclusion of some competition can vary the program. Often the competitive workload is lower than in the usual training routine. Because of this, athletes consider this to be load reduction. In addition, athletes are aware that nobody expects their personal best in such events that diversify hard training work. Inclusion of the restorative microcycle can be planned in advance or administered individually for athletes as they approach their upper limits of adaptation. Inclusion of a contrast aerobic (or strength-aerobic) mini-block makes it possible to prolong the attenuated training residuals and partly restore athletes for subsequent high intensity training.

**Monitoring the training** is intended mainly to prevent excessive fatigue accumulation and overtraining. It is important to monitor performance in the training program and to evaluate current achievements in sport-specific exercises. The general approach to this is presented in Table 3.11.

**Table 3.11**

**Major characteristics and indicators when monitoring the training in the transmutation mesocycle**

| Major characteristics | Indicators | Comments |
|---|---|---|
| Workload performance | Total volume of exercises<br>Partial volume of intense exercises<br>Outcomes of key-workout | It is important to know that athletes perform the planned work with respect to key-workouts and if there are any individual drawbacks |
| Targeted (sport-specific) abilities | Results in sport-specific exercises<br>Results attained in key-workouts | In non-measurable sports, qualitative evaluation is highly desirable |
| Training responses | Resting Heart Rate<br>Self-estimation of fatigue, stress, sleep, muscle soreness<br>Blood urea and CPK<br>Body mass, muscle mass<br>Fat component<br>Blood lactate after the trials and exercises of particular interest | Maximal workloads elicit maximal training responses, which should be taken as feedback. Subjective ratings of fatigue, stress, sleep and muscle soreness give the coach valuable information. Of course, much confidence between the coach and athlete is very important. |

It should be emphasized that dosage and the upper limits of adaptation are the biggest problems in the transmutation mesocycle. In this training cycle the highest sport-specific workloads are concentrated. Execution of these workloads substantially determines each athlete's individual progress. However, it is very difficult to determine the upper limit of adaptation that athletes should not exceed. Even evaluation of the hormonal state and other blood markers does not unequivocally guarantee a timely diagnosis of overtraining.

One of the most comprehensive definitions of overtraining was given by ex-world record holder and Olympic champion runner and sport physiologist, Peter Snell. He stated that, "Overtraining may be regarded as a state in which performance diminishes while the level of training is maintained or increased" (Snell, 1990). According to this explanation, the person who makes decisions about overtraining is the coach. From the coach's viewpoint, it is very important to recognize the generally accepted warning signals of the early phases of overtraining such as: (1) an increase in resting HR of more than 5 beats/min over a three-five day period; (2) persistent or rapid decrease of body mass; (3) persistent increased rate of general fatigue; (4) persistent increased rate of muscle soreness; (5) persistent increased rate of sleep disturbances (Burke et al., 1990; Hooper et al., 1995).

**Case study**. Nineteen elite swimmers were monitored during a 6-month period of preparation using a large battery of blood and urine markers, hormones, CPK, resting blood pressure and HR, and event-specific all-out tests with blood lactate determination. In addition, all swimmers made daily entries in their log-books of swim volume, time of dry-land workout and subjective ratings of stress, fatigue, sleep quality and muscle soreness on a scale of 1 (very, very low or good) to 7 (very, very high or bad). During the study three athletes were diagnosed as overtrained. However, the difference between stale and non-stale swimmers was not reflected in any blood, urine or other markers during mid- or late-season. Nevertheless, the differences were revealed quite significantly through fatigue and muscle soreness ratings. Moreover, the multi-component statistical model embracing the mean ratings of stress, fatigue, sleep quality and muscle soreness was able to predict changes in competitive performance. Interestingly, the use of a larger battery of indicators did not increase the accuracy of prediction (Hooper et al., 1995)

This example shows that sometimes even simple inexpensive methods (i.e. subjective ratings of stress, fatigue, sleep quality and muscle soreness), if used systematically and responsibly, provide effective monitoring of training that is particularly desirable in the high-load transmutation mesocycle.

### 3.2.3. Realization mesocycle

Traditionally, the realization mesocycle is termed the *taper*. In traditional periodization the taper is used prior to important competitions and is intended to stimulate better performance. According to the Block Periodization concept, the realization mesocycle forms the concluding phase of each training stage and, therefore, its function is broader. It is directed to attaining peak-performance and thus does not differ from the usual tapering technique. However, this mesocycle also concludes a carefully designed program consisting of several training stages in which all the important components are intentionally developed (see Figure 1.8).

The training stages in early- mid- and late season are not identical. Correspondingly, the realization mesocycles also differ depending on the level and importance of the forthcoming competition. This determines the essential characteristics of the mesocycle such as its duration, reduction of workloads, emotional tension of athletes, etc. These particulars are summarized in Table 3.12 and are considered briefly.

The transmutation mesocycle, in which maximal amounts of workloads are performed leads into the realization mesocycle. Consequently, athletes start the mesocycle when they are fatigued. Because of this the first objective is to provide and facilitate restoration and ultimately to attain the supercompensation state at the time of competition. It is important to remember that the targeted abilities, which should be the focus of the mesocycle program, demand high sensitivity and reactivity of the central and peripheral nervous systems, availability of energy resources and mental concentration. These prerequisites for proper development are seen in well rested athletes. Therefore, reduction of workload level is of paramount importance at the initiation of the realization program.

**Table 3.12**

**Major characteristics and particulars of the realization mesocycle**

| Major characteristics | Particulars | Comments |
|---|---|---|
| Aims | Peak-performance attainment, full restoration prior to competition, completing the training stage program | Demands for peaking depend on level and importance of forthcoming competition |
| Targeted abilities | Maximal speed (quickness), event specific tactics, readiness to compete | Well rested athletes are more able to effectively develop these abilities that require greater reactivity and concentration |
| Workload level | Much lower than in preceding mesocycles | There are various approaches to reducing workload level |
| Duration | One-three weeks | Depends on importance of competition and sport-specific factors |
| Techno-tactical improvement | The use of sport-specific modeled exercises (tasks) | These tasks have to form proper techno-tactical competitive performance |
| Emotional tension and anxiety | Elevation, pending the competition | Extent of elevation depends on the level of the forthcoming competition |
| Monitoring the training | Follow-up time-trials, evaluation of techno-tactical execution, training responses and level of restoration | The controls are focused on  a) integrative sport-specific estimates; b) most important individual traits and features |
| Nutrition | The use of nutritional supplements and control of energy intake | This is intended to produce an ergogenic effect and to prevent unfavorable changes in body mass and composition |

There are different approaches as to how the workloads can be reduced. The salient factor that affects the rate of workload reduction is duration of the mesocycle. A short mesocycle demands a fast workload decrease, a more prolonged mesocycle can be planned with a gradual reduction of workload level. The duration itself, is extremely important and sensitive. A long-duration mesocycle can lead athletes to detraining while an excessively short mesocycle may not be sufficient to restore and develop event-specific abilities. This contradiction was specifically noted (Mujika et al., 2004).

Simulation and enhancement of techno-tactical competitive behavior is an obligatory component of the realization mesocycle in many sports. Despite the striking specificity of various sports, the general idea of techno-tactical simulation is very similar – adjusting athletes to the planned or expected competitive behavior. Consequently, techno-tactical simulation programs should meet the following demands: (1) the competitive situation (race pattern, tactical combination, techno-tactical task etc.)  should as closely reproduced as possible in the exercise; (2) the level of athletes' concentration should approximate competitive levels; and (3) the number of simulations should be sufficient to attain stable and reliable techno-tactical skills. The typical techno-tactical tasks and their dosage in the realization mesocycle for qualified kayakers are presented in Table 3.13

**Table 3.13**

**Techno-tactical race simulation in a two-week realization mesocycle for qualified kayakers**

| Typical tasks for techno-tactical race simulation | Total number |
|---|---|
| Quasi-competitive race performance | 4-6 |
| Race simulation in broken series (four quarters divided by 20s breaks) | 8-12 |
| Selective simulation of the initial quarter of the race | 10-16 |
| Selective simulation of the mid-distance race pattern (two mid-quarters) | 8-12 |
| Simulation of the pre-event warm-up program | 3-5 |

Emotional tension and anxiety are attributes of pre-event preparation.  Their occurrence is seen mostly later in the season, when the importance of the competitions and the need to do well in them is greatest.  Keep in mind the contradictory impact of pre-event tapering on the emotional state of athletes. There is considerable evidence that workload reduction during the taper causes a remarkable improvement in mood associated mainly with improved recovery (see review by Mujika et al., 2004). However, pre-competition anxiety can change this trend dramatically at least in terms of two general factors: (1) a moderate level of anxiety facilitates performance and positively affects athletes' behavior, while excessive anxiety detracts from performance; (2) the effects of such emotional stimulation depend on the athletes' level, that is elite athletes benefit more than sub-elite from increased anxiety, whereas mid-class athletes can be sharpened by emotional tension (Raglin & Wilson, 2000).

Monitoring the training has a number of mesocycle-specific features that are associated with the dominant training modalities and the particulars of pre-competition preparation (See Table 3.14).

**Table 3.14**

**Major characteristics and indicators for use in monitoring the training in the realization mesocycle**

| Major characteristic | Indicator | Comments |
|---|---|---|
| Workload performance | Total number of sprint repetitions Total number of sport-specific simulations Total number of quasi-competitive performances | All these characteristics should be compared to the plan and individual history of each athlete. They can assess the quality of performance |
| Targeted abilities | Results in maximal speed tests Results in event simulation tests Relevant techno-tactical estimates | It is important that the test outcomes are comparable with similar preceding mesocycles |
| Training responses | Heart Rate and Blood lactate after the relevant exercises Resting Heart Rate Effort perception CPK and blood urea level | Acute post-exercise response characterizes individual reserves and perfection trend. CPK and blood urea indicate the level of restoration |
| Athlete's state | Sleep quality and mood state Body mass Fat component | Sleep and mood questionnaire can be used. Body mass and fat are of special interest in sports having weight categories. |

Although the realization mesocycles contained in the annual cycle are not identical, the similarity of the monitoring programs provides a number of visible benefits for athlete preparation:
- The coach can select, check and validate the entire set of tests and indicators;
- Individual norms for each athlete can be established;
- Athletes can learn about their individual responses in order to better adjust to more stressful situations as the target competition approaches;
- Methods of self-regulation, mental training and body mass reduction (if necessary) can be determined in advance and adjusted individually.

Nutrition during the realization mesocycle should be given special attention especially in regard to balancing dietary intake and energy expenditure. As was emphasized, workload reduction is characteristic of this mesocycle. Correspondingly, energy expenditure decreases significantly while athletes' nutritional habits often remain unchanged. As a result, energy intake can surpass energy expenditure causing a noticeable increase in the fat component.

---

**Case study**. Twenty highly qualified male long-distance triathletes were monitored during a four-week mesocycle with high workloads and a subsequent two-week taper mesocycle with reduced workloads. Body mass, body fat, energy intake and expenditure were evaluated. It was found that the average energy intake remained at the same level, but energy expenditure decreased during the taper mesocycle by up to 69.3% (Figure 3.10). Mean body mass of the group didn't change but body fat mass increased by 4.3%. The imbalance of dietary intake and energy expenditure caused remarkable fat accumulation. However, it is also possible that their muscle mass decreased as well while body mass remained at the previous level. Therefore, body mass as an indicator of the anthropometric state, is not always reliable. The pre-competition reduction of training workloads requires attention to nutrition, which should correspond to the decreased energy expenditure (based on Margaritis et al., 2003).

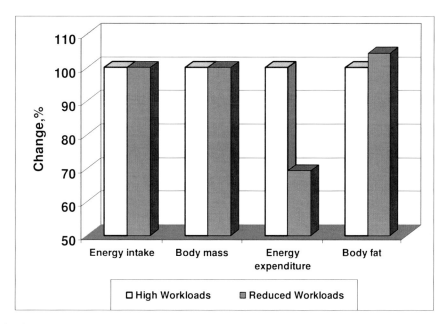

**Figure 3.10.** Changes in energy intake and expenditure, body mass and fat caused by pre-competition reduction of training workloads in qualified triathletes (based on Margaritis et al., 2003).

In conclusion, the realization mesocycle definitely has the lowest level of workloads but the level of emotional tension can be much higher than during the usual training routine. Consequently, this emotional factor can substantially modify both the athletes' behavior and training responses.

## 3.3. Training stage

According to Block Periodization, three consecutive mesocycle-blocks form a single training stage. Its length depends on the duration of each mesocycle and varies from 4-10 weeks. As was already noted (1.2.3), the training stage reconstructs the entire annual cycle in miniature. This allows for the consecutive development of basic abilities (as in the preparatory period), specific abilities (as in the competitive period), and integrative readiness for event-specific performance. The most favorable carry-over of residual training effects makes it possible to attain the optimal combination of basic, special and event-specific abilities as needed at the moment of competition (Figure 1.8). However, if the training design is based solely on the length of training residuals, it will be extremely rigid and inflexible. There are also other factors influencing training residuals and additional methods to prolong them.

### 3.3.1. Competition in the training stage.

It is well known that not all competitions are planned for peak performance. Some of them include extraordinarily high workloads to break the training routine and to add emotional diversity to the preparation. With this aim in mind, competition can be included in the accumulation and transmutation mesocycles. However, their influence is unequivocal. Highly intense competitions produce profound physical and emotional stress. The secretion of stress hormones like catecholamines and cortisol, modulate the athletes' metabolic response and reinforce the catabolic process (Viru & Viru, 2001). As a result, muscle mass and maximum strength can decrease.

Moreover, the highly intense anaerobic glycolitic efforts typical in competition suppress the activity of aerobic enzymes and the oxidative process in the mitochondria (Volkov, 1986). This impairment of aerobic fitness has been noted for some time by prominent coaches rather intuitively. They added special aerobic workloads to restore and revitalize the athletes after competition. A recent publication elucidates this negative effect of competition because of the shortened training residuals (Issurin & Lustig, 2004).

**Case study**. The preparation of multi- Olympic and World swimming champion Alexandre Popov was monitored using an incremental stepwise swimming test. His anaerobic threshold speed was determined at a blood lactate level of 4 mM and a speed producing 8 mM, as the lower limit of highly intense glycolitic workloads. These indicators were evaluated at the beginning of the mesocycle with highly concentrated aerobic workloads, ten days after this evaluation, and a few days after the competition in which Alexandre performed several times (Figure 3.11). In the initial stage of this study the remarkable gain in both anaerobic threshold speed and speed corresponding to 8 mM was noted. However, upon measurement of these factors again after competition, a substantial decrease was seen. This can be attributed to shortened training residuals, induced by the previous program (adapted from Pyne & Touretski,1993).

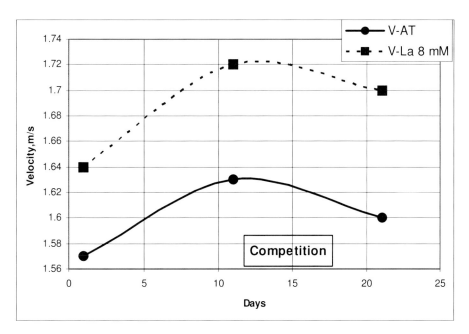

**Figure 3.11** The changes in anaerobic threshold (V-AT) and speed (velocity) at a
lactate level of 8 mM (V-La 8 mM) induced by the aerobic mesocycle and
participation in competition by Olympic champion Alexandre Popov
(based on data from Pyne and Touretski, 1993, published by Issurin & Lustig, 2004)

To conclude this section, the following relevant factors are worth noting:

1) Incorporating mid- and low-level competitions in the training stage is an
   important and meaningful component of the entire preparation;

2) Competitive performances elicit superior and profound athletes' responses that
   enrich the spectrum of adaptation to the training routine. However;

3) Highly intense competitive efforts bring about secretion of stress hormones
   that modulate metabolic and hormonal responses and shorten the residual
   training effects of the preceding mesocycle. This should be taken into account
   in the subsequent program.

### 3.3.2. How to prolong the residual training effects

Inasmuch as the training stage is a sequence of three mesocycle-blocks, the
crucial factor that restricts the length of a particular stage is the duration of the
residual training effects after the first accumulation mesocycle which lasts about 30
days (Table 1.6). This timing determines the total duration of the second and third
mesocycles, which should not be longer than the training residuals of the aerobic and
strength workloads, i.e., one month. However, in many sports the transmutation

mesocycle is directed at reinforcing anaerobic glycolitic abilities, which takes three-four weeks. In addition, the duration of the realization mesocycle (taper) can last about two weeks. The duration of both of these mesocycles (about five weeks) exceeds the time of the strength-aerobic training residuals that may cause the athletes to approach the targeted competition at a reduced level of basic abilities.

It is obvious that some special measures should be undertaken to prolong the training residuals of the strength-aerobic program. This prolongation can be attained by additional supporting workouts for aerobic endurance and/or muscular strength. But, such additions are not successful. The highly intense transmutation mesocycle strongly suppresses the immediate effect of aerobic training and the anabolic strength exercises require sufficient recovery that cannot be provided. Apparently, what should be inserted in the mesocycle is not several additional workouts but a special compact mini-block (short microcycle), in order to prolong training residuals. This principal approach is displayed in Figure 3.12.

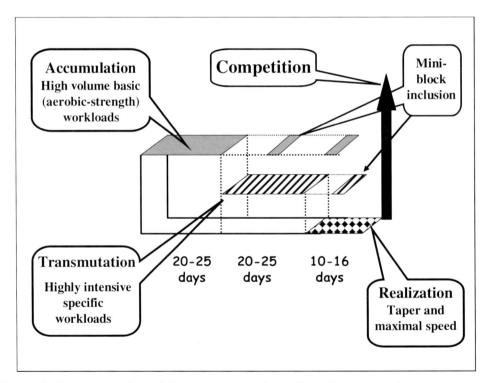

**Figure 3.12.** Prolongation of the residual training effects by means of appropriate mini-block inclusions (Issurin & Lustig, 2004)

> **Example**. Imagine a situation in which two targeted competitions have a
> five-week interval between them (this situation is very typical for kayaking
> where the European and World championships are separated by an interval of
> five-six weeks). In this case of inflexible time limits, you can plan 10-14 days for
> accumulation, 10-14 days for transmutation, and 8-10 days for the realization
> mesocycles. Here you need not include mini-blocks because the training
> residuals following the accumulation mesocycle surpass the competition.
> Another situation occurs when you are forced to plan a training stage for a period
> of 7-9 weeks (this situation is very typical of pre-Olympic preparation in several
> sports where the international calendar has no competitions scheduled before the
> major event). In this case, it is reasonable to plan longer mesocycles and the
> inclusion of mini-blocks would be necessary.

**Summary**

Microcycles, as the shortest training cycles, are differentiated in three
principle ways, loading, competing and recovery. The microcycles devoted to loading
differ according to load level. There is *adjustment* that serves to adapt athletes to
increasing workloads, *loading* that is used to develop athletic abilities, and *impact* that
employs extreme training stimuli. The competing microcycle contains the *pre-competitive* microcycle, which prepares the athlete for forthcoming competitions and
the *competitive* microcycle, where the athlete takes part in the competition. The
recovery microcycle consists of a special *restoration* microcycle. The microcycles can
be managed with respect to different load variations. More specifically, one-, two-,
and three-peak designs can be executed.

Presented in this chapter are microcycles focusing on (a) aerobic (strength-aerobic) abilities, (b) highly intense anaerobic workloads, (c) explosive strength in
highly coordinated exercises, and (d) pre-competitive training. These microcycles
have guidelines for structuring the microcycle. A number of general rules for
constructing the microcycle are as follows: (1) priority of the most meaningful key-workouts (2) interaction of successive workouts (3) sharing of restoration means (4)
initiating and peaking training workloads, and (5) monitoring the training.

The three types of mesocycles proposed by the Block Periodization Concept are considered with respect to duration, content and monitoring of training. Specifically, the *accumulation, transmutation* and *realization* mesocycles are described with respect to the sequencing of various microcycles. Also covered is fatigue accumulation that is particularly pronounced in the transmutation mesocycle, the selection of appropriate tasks and exercises, and determination of the most adequate means of monitoring several mesocycles. It is important to remember that athletes' self-estimation of training response in their log-book can provide valuable information for preventing excessive fatigue and even overtraining. Subjective ratings of stress, fatigue, quality of sleep and muscle soreness on a scale of 1 (very, very low or good) to 7 (very, very high or bad) are recommended for systematic use.

The training stage, consisting of three sequenced mesocycles, reconstructs the annual cycle in miniature, where training stimuli are focused first on basic abilities, second on more specific abilities, and third on integrative readiness for event-specific performance. It is essential to remember that competitive performances and emotional strain can shorten the training residuals of the preceding mesocycle. This phenomenon was considered through a case-study example of multi- Olympic champion Alexander Popov, whose anaerobic threshold speed decreased significantly after competition. Inclusion of special compact mini-blocks (short microcycles) can prolong the residual training effects of the preceding mesocycle. Thus, aerobic mini-blocks can be inserted in the transmutation mesocycle and a highly intense anaerobic mini-block can be incorporated within the realization mesocycle.

**References for Chapter 3**

Astrand, P., Rodahl, K., Dahl, H.A., Stromme, S.B. (2003). *Textbook of work physiology: Physiological bases of exercise*. 4th Ed. New York: McGraw-Hill.

Baker, D. (2001). The effects of an in-season of concurrent training on the maintenance of maximal strength and power in professional and college-aged rugby league football players. *J Strength Cond Res*, 15(2), 172-177.

Bompa, T. (1999) *Periodization: Theory and methodology of training* (4th ed.). Champaign, IL: Human Kinetics.

Bompa,T., Carrera, M. (2003) *Periodization Training for Sports*, 2nd Edition. Champaign, IL: Human Kinetics

Bondarchuk, A. P. (1986). *Training of track and field athletes.* Kiev: Health Publisher (Zdorovie)

Bouchard, C. (1986). Genetics of aerobic power and capacity. In.: Malina RM and Bouchard C. (Eds.) *Sport and Human Genetics*, Champaign, IL: Human Kinetics, p. 59-88.

Burke, E.R., Faria, I., White J.A. (1990). In: Reilly T, Secher N., Snell P. and Williams C. (Eds.), *Physiology of sports.* London: E.&F.N.Spon, p.173-216.

Cardinale, M.and Stone, M.H. (2006). Is testosterone influencing explosive performance? *J Strength Cond Res*, 20 (1), 103-107.

Chesley, A., MacDougal,J.D., Tarnopolsky, M.A. et al. (1992). Changes in human muscle protein synthesis after resistance exercises. *J Appl Physiol*, 73, 1383-1389.

Dick, F. (1980). *Sport training principles*. London: Lepus Books.

Fleck, S.J. and Kraemer, W.J. (1997). *Designing resistance training programs* (2nd edition). Champaign, IL: Human Kinetics.

Hooper, S.L., Mackinnon, L.T., Howard, A. et al., (1995). Markers for monitoring overtraining and recovery. *Med Sci Sports Exercises*, 27, 106-112.

Issurin V. (2003). Aspekte der kurzfristigen Planung im Konzept der Blockstruktur des Trainings. *Leistungsport*. 33: 41-44.

Issurin V., Lustig G. (2004). Klassifikation, Dauer und praktische Komponenten der Resteffekte von Training. *Leistungsport*. 34, 55-59.

Komi, P. (1988). The musculosceletal system. In: Dirix, A., Knuttgen, H.,G., Tittel, K.(Eds.). *The Olympic book of sports medicine. Vol. I of the Encyclopedia of Sports Medicine*. Blackwell Scientific Publications, 15-39.

Kubukeli Z, Noakes T, Dennis S. (2002). Training techniques to improve endurance exercise performances. *Sports Med*, 32, 489-509.

Margaritis, I., Palazetti, S., Rousseau, A-S., et al. (2003). Antioxydant supplementation and tapering exercise improve exercise-induced antioxydant response. J Am Coll Nutrition, 22, 147-156.

Martin, D. (1980). *Grundlagen der Trainingslehre*. Verlag Karl Hoffmann, Schorndorf

Mujika, I., Padilla,S., Pyne, D.,and Busso, T. (2004). Physiological changes associated with the pre-event taper in athletes. *Sports Med*, 34, 891-927.

Noakes, T. (2000). Physiological models to understand exercise fatigue and the adaptations that predict or enhance athletic performance. *Scand J Med Sci Sports*, 10, 123-145.

Newton, R., Rogers, R.A., Volek, J.S. et al. (2006). Four weeks of optimal load resistance training at the end of season attenuates declining jump performance of women volleyball players. *J Strength Cond Res*, 20(4), 955-961.

Platonov, V.N. (1997). *General theory of athletes' preparation in the Olympic sports*. Kiev: "Olympic Literature". (Russian).

Platonov,V., Fesenko, S. (1990). *Preparation of the best world athletes*. Moscow: Fizkultura i sport. (Russian).

Pyne, D.B., Touretski, G. (1993). An analysis of the training of Olympic Sprint Champion Alexandre Popov. *Australian Swim Coach*, 10 (5), 5-14.

Raglin, J.S.,Wilson, G.S. (2000). Psychology on endurance performance. In: Shephard R.J. and Astrand P.-O. (Eds.). *Endurance in Sport. Volume II of the Encyclopaedia of Sports Medicine*. Oxford: Blackwell Science, p. 211-218.

Saltin, B. (1986). Anaerobic capacity: past, present, and perspective. In: Saltin B. (Ed.). *Biochemistry of Exercise VI*. Champaign, IL: Human Kinetics, p.387-398.

Sharobajko, I.V. (1984). *Specialized fitness training of female kayakers with respect to their movement particulars*. Thesis of Ph.D. dissertation. Moscow: All-Union Research Sport Institute.

Snell, P. (1990). Middle distance running. In: Reilly T, Secher N., Snell P. and Williams C. (Eds.), *Physiology of sports*. London: E.&F.N.Spon, p.101-120.

Starischka, S. (1988). *Trainingsplanung. Studienbrief der Trainerakademie Koeln*, Schorndorf: Hoffmann.

Viru, A. (1995). *Adaptation in sports training.* Boca Raton, FL: CRC Press

Viru, A., Karelson, K, and Smirnova, T. (1992).Stability and variability in hormonal responses to prolonged exercises. *Int J Sports Med*, 13, 230-235.

Viru, A.and Viru, M. (2001). *Biochemical monitoring of sport training.* Champaign, IL: Human Kinetics.

Volkov, N. (1986). Biochemistry of sport. In: Menshikov V. and Volkov, N. (Eds.), *Biochemistry*. Moscow: Fizkultura i sport, p.267-381.

Wilmore,J.H., Costill, D.L. (1993). *Training for sport and activity. The physiological basis of the conditioning process.* Champaign, IL: Human Kinetics.

Yessis, M. (2006). *Build a Better Athlete*. Terre Haute, IN: Equilibrium Books.

Zatsiorsky, V.M.(1995). *Science and practice of strength training*. Champaign, IL: Human Kinetics.

# Chapter 4

Ivan Klementiev
Olympic champion, seven-time world champion in canoe,
member of national parliament of Latvia

# Chapter 4

# Long-term preparation

Long-term preparation concerns periods lasting one year and more. From this viewpoint three major aspects of long-term preparation demand proper consideration. They are the annual cycle, multi-year preparation of qualified athletes, including the quadrennial cycle, and multi-year preparation of juniors. This chapter will present and clarify the basic positions and planning guidelines pertaining to these three aspects.

## 4.1 The annual cycle

The planning of the annual cycle in terms of Block Periodization was previously described in general terms. Special attention should be given to the technology of planning and guidelines for training design.

### 4.1.1 Goals, objectives and basic directions of the annual plan

When dealing with experienced athletes, annual goal setting and establishing objectives frequently seem superfluous. Even a brief analysis, however, will show that they are important. Goal setting for annual preparation demonstrates the coach's responsibility and stimulates athletes to undertake serious obligations. Concrete

129

training objectives indicate the gains in technique, motor fitness, mental toughness etc. that should be made in order to attain the main goal. The motivation and confidence of the athletes will be higher and more stable when they can clearly see the ways in which the annual preparation can be made more effective (use of new training methods, enhanced monitoring, employment of new equipment etc.). And finally, the coach and athlete should discover the athlete's hidden reserves, which when liberated, will facilitate better performance (Table 4.1).

**Table 4.1**

**The content and sequencing of goal setting in annual cycle planning**

| Factors | Content | Comments |
|---------|---------|----------|
| Goal | The desired and expected main outcome of annual preparation should be set | The goal should be realistic and formulated concretely (rank, result, position in team etc.) |
| Objectives | The objectives refer to essential components of athletic preparedness and propose ways of discerning gains in the athletes' abilities | The objectives can be expressed as gains in technical, physical, tactical and mental preparedness |
| Basic directions | The basic directions of improving preparation can be pinpointed. | The set directions can concern training methods, organization, equipment etc. |
| Available reserves | Hidden reserves can usually be found from analysis of preparation and performance | It is necessary to convince the athletes that the noted reserves can be actualized |

Unfortunately not every season ends successfully. In such cases the coach starts planning for the next year by analyzing the failures that occurred. The simplest way of conducting such an analysis is by seeking the external fatal factors affecting the athletes' performance. The array of possible fatal reasons is large: bad draw, low judgment, sudden wind or rain, earthquake etc. A tactic employed by a great coach, is to explain to unsuccessful athletes that the training program was excellent and that they (the athletes) were completely responsible for the failure. The correct approach to analysis assumes mutual responsibility of coach and athlete for both successful and unsuccessful seasons. This is important in order for the athletes to develop a confident attitude in regard to goal setting for the next season.

### 4.1.2 Constructing the annual program

Coaches put together annual programs based on their own experience, knowledge and common sense. However, the Block Periodization approach implies specific demands to planning that can be described as sequencing certain steps (Table 4.2).

**Table 4.2**

**Step sequence in constructing an annual training program**

| No | Steps | Comments |
|---|---|---|
| 1 | Determining the target and mandatory competitions | Usually these events are taken from international/national and/or regional calendars |
| 2 | Determination of the terms and duration of training stages and periods | The stages are determined in terms of target competitions and methodology |
| 3 | Division of training stages into several meso- and microcycles | Mesocycle purpose and duration should be specified |
| 4 | Planning for additional competitions and trials | The competitions and trials are necessary to finalize the training stages and to diversify the preparatory program |
| 5 | Planning the training camps | Objectives, terms and places for camps should be specified |
| 6 | Planning of the medical and sport-specific tests | The initial medical exam is planned for early season |
| 7 | Calculation of integrative workload characteristics per month | These characteristics can relate to total mileage, number of lifts, throws etc. |
| 8 | Calculation of integrative workload characteristics for the annual cycle | Comparison with previous years helps to reveal "weak" points of the plan |
| 9 | Correction of plan following revelation of "weak" points | As a rule, the first version needs correction and this operation is obligatory |

As can be seen in Table 4.2, the initial step requires determination of the most important competitions (Figure 4.1). These events determine the division of the season into stages and periods. The optimal design assumes planning for peak-performance at the end of the training stage (see example in Figure 4.2). The subdivision of the annual cycle into periods follows general logic and is less important than in traditional periodization.

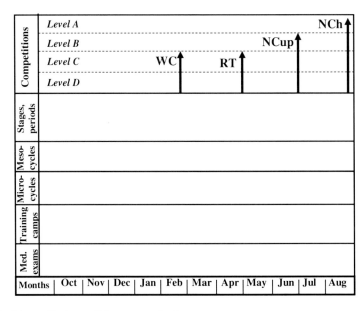

**Figure 4.1.** Compilation of the annual plan:

1ˢᵗ step – determination of targeted (level A) and mandatory competitions (Levels B and C); NCh – national championship, NCup – national Cup, RT – regional trials, WC – winter cup

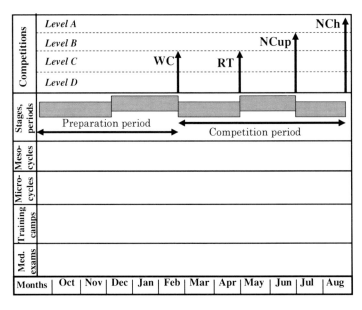

**Figure 4.2.** Compilation of the annual plan:

2ⁿᵈ step – determination of terms and duration of training stages and periods. In the optimal design, important competitions are scheduled at the end of the stage.

The next two steps contain a division of training stages into several meso- and microcycles, and the scheduling of additional competitions, which are planned for early- and mid-season (Figure 4.3).

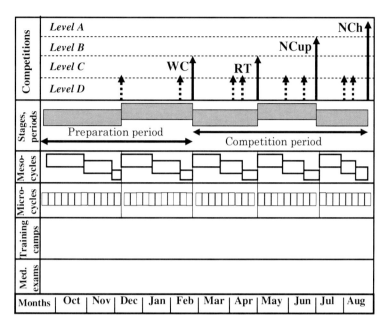

**Figure 4.3.** Compilation of the annual plan:

3rd and 4<sup>th</sup> steps – division of training stages into several meso- and microcycles, planning of additional competitions and trials.

The 5<sup>th</sup> step prescribes the planning of training camps to better realize the specific objectives of certain block mesocycles. This also relates to the use of altitude preparation (chapter 5).

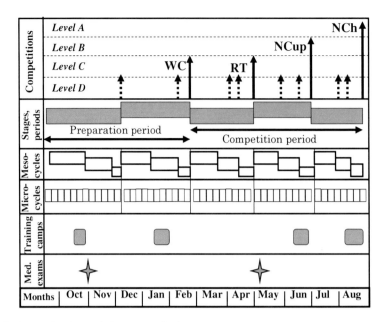

**Figure 4.4.** Compilation of the annual plan:

5th and 6th steps – planning of training camps and medical examinations (sport-specific tests are not displayed).

The next step in annual planning is the calculation of integrative monthly workload characteristics. Parameters such as total number of workouts, total mileage, number of bouts and matches, number of quasi-competitive performances etc. can be successfully planned per month. The summation of all the monthly characteristics yields the integrative annual workloads, which can then be compared with previous years and the data of other athletes. Usually this whole planning process does not lead to the final version of annual program. It must first be reviewed by the administration, colleagues and athletes and with repeated analysis, will lead to corrections in specific details such as the timing and duration of training camps, cancellation of competitions etc. The corrected program then receives the final version status that is used for realization.

### 4.1.3 General trends in workload planning within the annual cycle of preparation

The general tendency in annual planning is to reserve the most specialized and rigorous workloads for the training period preceding the most important competition. The Block Periodization approach with its multi-peak preparation does not contradict this position although it exploits it in its own way.

134

Despite the variety of training conditions and specificity of different sports, several common trends in program compilation can be seen (Table 4.3).

**Table 4.3**

**Seasonal trends in compilation of the annual cycle training program**

| Characteristics | Early season | Mid season | Late season |
|---|---|---|---|
| Dominant training methods in the accumulation mesocycle | Continuous, uniform and alternating exercises | Continuous and slow interval exercises | Strictly programmed interval exercises |
| Dominant training methods in the transmutation mesocycle | Continuous, alternating and interval training | Mostly interval exercises | Strictly programmed interval exercises |
| Diversity of fitness program | Wide range of fitness exercises | Restricted range of exercises | Mostly specialized exercises selected |
| Organizational forms of workouts | Higher contribution of individual workouts | Lower contribution of individual workouts | Use of strictly programmed workouts |
| Use of restorative means | Mostly exercises--stretching, relaxation, low intensity aerobics etc. | Higher contribution of physiotherapy, massage, mental training, nutritional supplements | Employment of the most effective individually selected restorative means |
| Use of competitive simulation forms | Periodically, not frequently | Systematically, more frequently | Higher contribution in training program |

The general tendency is to gradually increase workload specialization and mobilization of hidden reserves towards the target competition. The general rule in Block Periodization is that the training stages within the annual cycle should be similar but not identical. The mid season and particularly late season stages should be more rigorous, more strictly programmed and better managed. It is highly desirable that the most effective training and restorative means and drill combinations be reserved for the crucial periods in annual preparation. Physiologically, this gives the benefit of higher training responses prior to the most important events. Psychologically, it heightens the athletes' self-confidence as they know that they have additional reserves during the most stressful phase of their preparation.

Special attention should be given to the competitive component of annual preparation. Block Periodization gives great importance to competitions even in the early phase of the annual cycle for the following reasons:

1) competition completes each training stage and is a compulsory component of the training program;

2) the competition breaks the usual routine and brings out the very important element of athlete spirit;

3) the competition provides athletes with extraordinary training stimuli that can not be obtained from regular workloads.

It is worth noting that the competitive program varies during the season. It is good to diversify the competitions in early season, to bring the competition to event-specific standards in mid season, and to adhere to event-specific standards in late season. The reasons for such changes are two-fold. The competitions are a compulsory component of the annual program in early-, mid- and late season and a varied program of competition helps to diversify the training routine and restore athletes after the habitual event-specific format.

## 4.2 Quadrennial cycle of athletic preparation

Completion of the Olympic quadrennial cycle is usually followed by serious and detailed analysis of the Olympic performance including successes and failures. It is natural for great success to elicit enthusiasm and inspiration and for failure to cause dissatisfaction, criticism and a tendency to reform. Irrespective of sport-specificity and nationality, the challenge of post-Olympic analysis is to internalize positive experiences and reveal the reasons for sub-par performances. Based on the findings, a new preparatory plan is worked out. It is good when clear and concrete general objectives are determined for each stage of the quadrennial plan. An example of setting objectives can be found in the preparation of one of the most successful gymnastics team of Russia (Arkajev & Suchilin, 2004).

**Example.** The quadrennial cycle of the Russian gymnastics national team is subdivided into eight half-year stages. Each stage is directed to a specific general objective:

1.  Enhancement of sport-specific motor fitness

2.  Acquisition of new, highly complex technical skills and their hybrids

3.  Updating of combinations used in competition

4.  Further increases in sport-specific motor fitness

5.  Enhancement of technical mastery and attaining stable (reliable) performances

6.  Increase in performance quality, stability and stress tolerance.

7.  Final compilation of competition combinations, development of endurance for an entire program and selection of a duplicate Olympic squad

8.  Modeling of expected competitive conditions, attaining high competitive reliability and final selection of the Olympic National team.

Each of the above stages encompasses a complex evaluation of the cumulative training effect induced by the completed program.

This example shows that dividing the quadrennial cycle into separate stages is a matter of professional competence and depends on sport-specific conditions. Nevertheless, the division of the quadrennial cycle into four annual cycles is the most popular. In general, the main directions of quadrennial preparation, irrespective of sport, are presented in Table 4.4.

**Table 4.4**

**Athletic preparation within a quadrennial cycle**

| Year | Main directions of preparation |
|------|-------------------------------|
| 1st | Engagement and examination of new candidate, selection of coaches and other staff specialists, updating and correcting usual training means and methods, remodeling training repertory, formation of team spirit and camaraderie between athletes and staff. |
| 2nd | Further selection and approval of new candidates, acquisition of new techno-tactical skills, increase in training workloads, improving quality of training |
| 3rd | Attaining maximal level of training workloads, approving the annual cycle planned for the Olympic season and determining the individual performance characteristics for each team member |
| 4th | Stabilization of team make-up usually with the double Olympic squad; stabilization of workloads on the level of the preceding year, approval and stabilization of the competitive behavior and performance |

Let's consider the above directions with respect to training designed for athletes of different ages and levels of experience. Highly experienced top-level athletes require special attention during Olympic preparation both on national teams of leading sports countries, where coaches enjoy a large number of potential athletes, and on relatively small national teams, where the possibility of adding new successful team-members is very limited. The advantages of older and experienced athletes are obvious as they have a remarkable advantage in terms of basic and sport-specific knowledge, emotional control, stability of technical, techno-tactical skills and competitive behavior. They are usually high-authority persons who positively affect social climate and team spirit.

The disadvantages of having such athletes are also clear as they are approaching their biological limits in regard to training responses, i.e., they have less reactivity to training stimuli, they usually follow habitual training programs and do not like to change their training style and repertory. Older athletes perform with a lower training volume and need longer transition periods for physical and mental rehabilitation. In the first annual cycle of the quadrennial plan these athletes have a substantially lower total volume of exercises – about 15-20% less – than in the previous Olympic year (Figure 4.5).

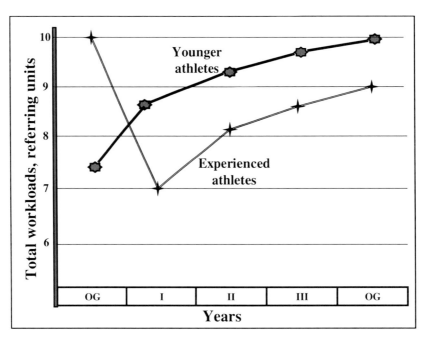

**Figure 4.5.** Quadrennial trend of total workloads in experienced athletes who took part in previous Olympics, and younger athletes preparing for the next Olympics.  OG – Olympic Games

138

Experienced, more aged athletes continue the quadrennial cycle with a gradual increase in training volume, which in any case is usually less than that for their younger counterparts. The model for the third annual cycle is based on the Olympic year for each category of athletes. Both aged and younger athletes increase the level of their training workloads and approach their maximum. Generally speaking, the third and fourth annual cycles should be very similar since coaches simulate the annual pre-Olympic training design one year before in order to provide the highest quality preparation at the end stage of the quadrennial cycle. In fact, the training workload level in the pre-Olympic season is usually higher than the year before for various reasons. This includes greater motivation, better conditions for training and restoration, greater budgets etc.

Younger athletes, who have not participated in the Olympic Games have typical characteristics. After being involved in Olympic preparations, their athletic motivation is greatly stimulated and they usually enjoy better training conditions that include more training camps, more qualified training partners, sometimes more experienced coaches etc. As a result, these athletes substantially increase their training workloads in comparison to the previous year. In the second and third annual cycles the training workloads continue to rise although at a smaller rate of increase.

From a methodological point of view, it is important to predict and plan development of the most relevant motor, technical and tactical abilities. For this, it is necessary to expand the corresponding model characteristics of these components of preparedness with respect to improvement rates during the quadrennial cycle.

## 4.3 Sport longevity of highly qualified athletes

Contemporary sport has many examples of highly successful athletes who continue their careers up to and past age thirty. This athletic longevity has been affected by many factors, such as high and stable motivation, proper style of behavior, improved training methodology, social support, financial stimulation, etc. In regard to the training itself, a number of age-related characteristics can be pinpointed irrespective of the sport involved (Table 4.5).

139

**Table 4.5**

**Preparation particulars for older and experienced high-performance athletes in comparison to their younger counterparts**

| Factor | Particulars | Comments |
|---|---|---|
| Annual cycle structure | Longer duration of transition period | Aged athletes need additional time for psychological and medical rehabilitation |
| Total training volume | 10-30% less than for younger athletes | Older athletes train more conscientiously and produce longer training residuals |
| Organizational forms | Higher contribution of individual training | Aged athletes need less supervision, show more initiative and independence |
| Restoration | Increased use of restorative means | Older athletes recover slower and often suffer from previous injuries |
| Equipment | More insistent and creative selection and approval of equipment | Aged athletes have their own demands about equipment. They are serious and consistent during their examination |
| Individual progress | Motor potential doesn't increase but can be utilized more effectively | Stabilization and reduction of several functions are compensated for by higher efficiency of athletic activity |

Of course, a number of additional social factors affect the preparation and behavior of aged athletes. Very often they combine their athletic preparation with professional activity and some odler athletes have families which substantially changes their mentality and life priorities. The preparation particulars can be illustrated using examples of two outstanding athletes who attained great results during their long athletic careers.

**Case study of long-term training workloads**. The world-famous canoeist, Olympic Champion Ivan Klementiev represented the USSR and from 1991, Latvia during four Olympic cycles. He earned one gold and two silver Olympic medals and seven World Championship gold medals. During a period of 19 years many aspects of his training were well documented with the most informative being total annual paddling volume (Figure 4.6). Analysis of the multi-year annual training volume reveals a number of salient points:

-- Maximal training volume was attained at age 21 when he trained with the USSR national squad.  Annual training volume tended to decrease despite periodic deviations in the following years;

-- Quantitative analysis of the average annual volume over quadrennial cycles when he took part in the Olympic Games reveals the following: ages 21-24 – 100%; ages 25-28 -88.2%; ages 29-32 – 77.4%, and ages 33-36 – 61%;

-- Analysis of periodic oscillations reveals a remarkable increase in training volume in the final years of the Olympic cycles with one exception.  In 1984, because of political, not methodological circumstances – instead of competing in the Los Angeles Olympics that was held in August, the athlete competed in a substitute regatta of socialist countries held in July.  As a result, the season was cut short by one month;

-- Reduction of the annual training volume is partly conditioned by longer transition periods that increased from one to three months during his career.

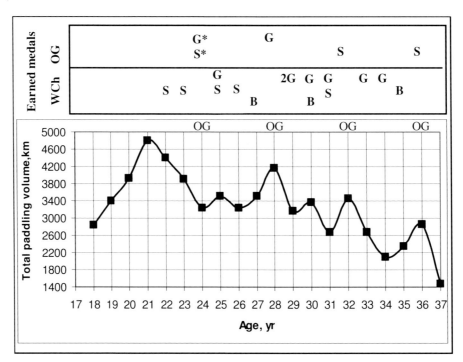

**Figure 4.6.** Long-term trend of annual paddling volume and personal achievements of Olympic and seven-time canoeing World Champion Ivan Klementiev (USSR, Latvia);

Key: OG – Olympic Games, WCh – World Championships, G – gold, S – silver, B – bronze medals, at age 24 the athlete competed in a regatta of socialist countries as an alternative to the Los Angeles Olympic Games

It should be emphasized that despite the constant decrease in total workloads, Ivan Klementiev continued to have extremely successful performances and after age 30 won four gold medals at the World Championships and two Olympic silver medals. Apparently, workload reduction was effectively compensated for by a higher quality of training. This training enhancement was associated with better preparation exploiting Block Periodization, a more conscious and effective selection of exercises, avoidance of non-compatible workload combinations, constant attention to restoration, and the use of a logical program of competition (Klementiev, 1994). This great athlete earned a Ph.D. degree, and has been a highly successful coach, serving on the national canoe squads of Poland and Spain.

As already stated, long-term preparation is characterized by a cumulative training effect, in which physiological evaluations are of special interest. Unfortunately, such data for multi-year training among elite athletes are very limited.

142

Therefore, the case study of legendary cyclist Lance Armstrong is unique and extremely interesting (Coyle, 2005).

---

**Case study of physiological changes during long-term preparation.** Lance Armstrong, world famous cyclist, became World Champion and seven-time Grand Champion of the Tour de France, the most famous and prestigious road race in the world. From ages 21 to 28 he was examined in a physiology laboratory for body composition, maximal oxygen uptake, maximal blood lactate and mechanical efficiency of pedaling. At age 24 he was diagnosed with testicular cancer and during a two year period he came through surgery and treatment that included chemotherapy. From ages 27-32 Lance Armstrong was victorious six times in the Tour de France, undoubtedly an incredible success in world sport.

During a seven year period, starting from age 21, the athlete's body weight increased slightly by 0.8 kg while lean body weight increased by 1.1 kg. The multi-year trend of physiological variables showed the following (Figure 4.7):

- the maximum oxygen uptake reached peak value at age 23, declined after medical treatment and did not reach the highest level until age 28 when he won the Tour de France;

- maximum heart rate decreased by 6 beat/min;

- mechanical efficiency, as the ratio of mechanical work to energy expended, increased by 8.8%;

- mechanical power obtained at an oxygen uptake of 5.0 l/min displayed a substantial increase of 18%.

It is worth noting that the final estimate of maximum oxygen uptake, 71 ml/kg/min, is inferior to the data of elite cyclists which approaches the level of 80 ml/kg/min (Padilla et al., 2000). It can be speculated that when Lance reduced his body weight prior to the races, the real level of maximum oxygen uptake per body weight became higher than previously. Nevertheless the study findings indicate that the individual progress of this great athlete was determined not by enlargement of his physiological potential but by its more efficient utilization. The physiological mechanism of this improved muscular efficiency is still unclear. The hypothetical contributors to such improvement can be associated with pronounced hypertrophy and improved contractility of slow muscle fibers, alteration in myosin ATPase activity, increased cycling efficiency induced by altitude training and enhanced pedaling technique.

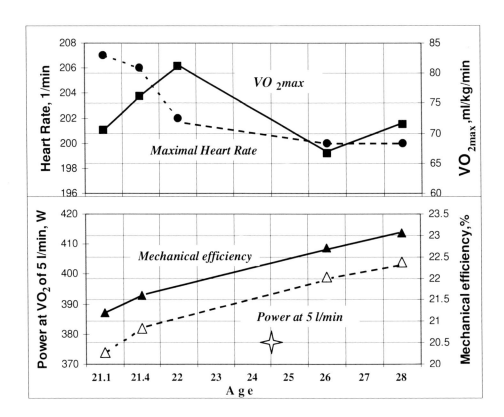

**Figure 4.7.** The long-term changes of several physiological indicators in cyclist Lance Armstrong (adapted from Coyle, 2005).

✦ - medical treatment including chemotherapy

It should be noted that Lance Armstrong attained enormous success after extremely serious surgery and medical treatment. His autobiography is an example of magnificent athletic and human fortitude (Armstrong, 2000). Of course, his athletic career and individual data are unique. In any case, the tendencies revealed in the study of Armstrong's progress are highly typical. Indeed, many highly qualified athletes approach their biological limits but continue to attain their best performances and even improve their athletic results. The main source of such individual progress is usually better utilization of their motor and physiological capabilities. This improved utilization can be conditioned by physiological, biomechanical and psychological factors, where individual creativity, self-confidence and athletic wisdom play a great role.

## 4.4 Long-term preparation of young athletes

The athletic career of both world-class and less successful athletes is highly dependent on the earlier period of long-term preparation that usually begins in childhood. The purview of this chapter restricts consideration of this matter, which is worthy of its own book. Nevertheless, the most relevant and generalized aspects of young athletes' long-term preparation will be presented. This includes the content and sequencing of different stages, the concept of sensitive periods in long-term preparation, and the basics for identifying gifted youngsters.

### 4.4.1 Stages and details of long-term preparation

The common approach to long-term preparation of athletes assumes that there are four separate stages (Table 4.6).

**Table 4.6.**

**Stages of long-term preparation and their general characteristics**

**(based on Issurin, 1994)**

| Stages | Number of years | Number of workouts per week | Duration of workouts in min | Yearly training volume in hours |
|---|---|---|---|---|
| Preliminary preparation | 1-3 | 3-4 | 45-60 | 120-170 |
| Initial specialization | 2-3 | 4-5 | 75-90 | 250-300 |
| Advanced specialization | 2-3 | 6-9 | 60-120 | 500-750 |
| Sports perfection | i.d.* | 6-12 | 70-150 | 750-1400 |

* individually dependent

The stage of preliminary preparation varies from one to three years depending on sport-specific demands and the age at which the athlete begins systematic training. Apparently the favorable ages for starting vary widely in different sports (Figure 4.8).

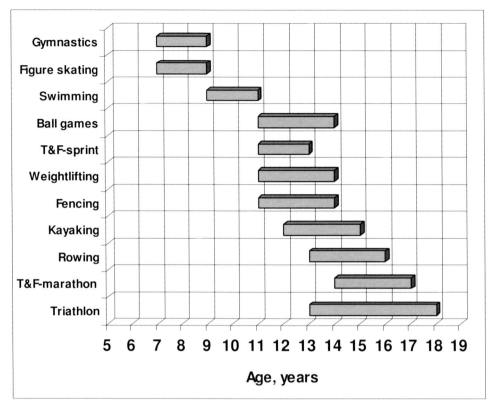

**Figure 4.8.** Favorable ages to start systematic preparation in different sports (adapted from Platonov & Sakhnovsky, 1988; the limits were updated on the basis of interviews with international experts in the respective sports).

Note: Ball games refers to team and dual sports.

The common tendency in contemporary sport is a reduction in age for children to begin preparation for specific sports. Various reasons explain this trend, such as the availability of high quality equipment designed for children (barbells, boats, paddles etc.), enhanced training conditions, popularization of sports activities for children by the media, and examples of world-known stars who started their sport preparation very early. This reduction in the starting age of training and competition has greatly affected the international and national sport organizations.

For instance, a few decades ago it was generally agreed that boys should begin weightlifting training no younger than age 14. Now the general practice worldwide is for schoolboys to take part in international weightlifting competitions at age 11 and even earlier. Of course, sport-specific demands strongly affect when newcomers can begin and the duration of their preliminary preparation. For example, many juniors with previous serious experience in swimming may start systematic triathlon training early. Thus, the duration of their preliminary preparation depends on how long it will take them to acquire cycling and running skills. This can take about one year. Therefore, the data presented in Figure 4.8 reflect worldwide practice but do not include special situations in which youngsters begin their training earlier or later.

The initial preliminary preparation stage is characterized mainly by all-round (multilateral), mostly attractive but not excessive workloads, where harmony between basic technical and fitness exercises is of utmost importance (Table 4.7). It is generally agreed that children with higher level motor abilities have visible benefits in acquiring new sport-specific skills. On the other hand, children with lower initial fitness levels may possess higher sensitivity to training stimuli and within a given time may equal or even surpass the leaders.

Therefore, a period of about one-two years of preliminary preparation is needed both to strengthen, interest, motivate, instill willingness to continue training in a selected sport, and to evaluate the predisposition and innate abilities of newcomers for a specific sport. Participation in competition is strongly recommended at this stage but in reasonable quantities and using a diversified competitive program. The training program as a whole is of great importance for forming and developing proper mental abilities that can decisively determine whether long-term preparation will continue.

**Table 4.7**

**Main training directions in the preliminary stage of preparing athletes**

| Abilities | Main training directions |
|---|---|
| Technical | Acquisition of sport-specific and general skills, development of specific and general coordination abilities |
| Physical | Multilateral (all-round) development of motor abilities with special emphasis on sport-specific skills and an increase in general training capacity |
| Tactical | Acquaintance with the tactical demands of the selected sport, acquisition of basic tactical knowledge and techno-tactical skills |
| Mental | Consolidation of interest in the selected sport, formation of stable motivation and conscientious will to continue preparation, adoption of fundamental moral principles of "fair play", team spirit etc. |

The second stage of long-term athletic preparation, known as initial specialization, is devoted to further development of sport-specific technical skills and motor abilities (Table 4.8). To be successful in these objectives it is critical that the coach fully comprehend technique of the skills and related physical abilities (Yessis, 2006). This is the period in which young athletes make their conscious selection of the most appropriate disciplines and events as the program of technical and physical preparation become more specialized. It is important at this time to adapt athletes to the training workloads typical of this sport. Participation in competition is an indispensable part of the overall preparation as it also provides an opportunity for coaches and athletes to assess levels of tactical and mental abilities, which need much attention.

**Table 4.8**

**Main training directions in the initial specialization stage for preparing athletes**

| Abilities | Main training directions |
|-----------|--------------------------|
| Technical | Further development of sport-specific skills and selection of the most favorable sport disciplines and events. Further increases in technical and coordination type abilities |
| Physical | More specialized development of motor abilities focusing on sport-specific demands. Adaptation to training workloads typical of this sport |
| Tactical | More profound learning of competitive rules and tactics, and further enhancement of tactical knowledge and techno-tactical skills |
| Mental | Acquisition of self-confidence and will power, formation of consciousness and responsibility in training situations and in competition, further improvement in motivation to train and compete in the selected sport |

The third stage of long-term preparation, termed advanced specialization, encompasses the period in which athletes attain the real bases of mastery. Usually it corresponds to the age at which athletes complete their junior preparation and join the adult athletes. Consequently, their technical and physical abilities should approach the level of qualified adults (Table 4.9). Concomitantly, training workloads increase substantially and may approach those of adult athletes.

It is worth noting that despite increased technical and motor abilities, juniors at this stage are still not completely mature and the use of maximal workloads should be restricted. In particular, administration of highly intense anaerobic glycolitic exercises requires complete control because highly qualified juniors can be overly ambitious in their training routines but not experienced enough in self-regulation of metabolic and muscular reactions. Nevertheless, participation in competition is of particular importance at this stage both as a part of the overall program and as an indispensable activity for strengthening motivation to achieve sports excellence and to acquire the extremely useful skills of emotional control and mental regulation. In addition, personal traits such as self-confidence and will power are no less important for successful athletic careers than proper techno-tactical and sport-specific motor abilities.

**Table 4.9**

**Main training directions in the advanced specialization stage**

| Abilities | Main training directions |
|-----------|--------------------------|
| Technical | Attaining effective technique in selected disciplines or events, establishing an individual technical style and elimination of individual technical drawbacks |
| Physical | Further enhancement of sport-specific motor abilities, formation of sufficient motor abilities for effective and individualized skill technique |
| Tactical | Formation of individualized tactical and techno-tactical skills, improvement of techno-tactical coordination |
| Mental | Developing the motivation to attain sports excellence, enhancement of emotional control, acquisition of mental regulatory skills, maintenance of high self-confidence and will power |

The fourth stage of long-term preparation, if an athlete achieves it, is the most variable in duration. For world-class stars such as Ivan Klementiev and Lance Armstrong this stage lasts almost twenty years. For the majority of high-performance athletes it encompasses four-seven years. During this time they enhance their preparedness and compete with high ambition. This stage is definitely the period of highest individual creativity. It is when experienced athletes can consciously contribute to their programs in terms of movement technique, motor fitness, tactics and strategy, and mental functioning (Table 4.10). Of course, the improvement rate in motor and technical abilities is much lower at this stage than previously. As was brought out in Table 4.5, the motor potential of aged and experienced athletes is enhanced mostly through better utilization.

**Table 4.10**

**Main training directions in the sports perfection stage**

| Abilities | Main training directions |
|---|---|
| Technical | Further enhancement of movement technique with special regard for individual style and particulars of the athlete |
| Physical | Attaining the highest level of sport-specific motor abilities and their improved utilization in an effective manner |
| Tactical | Attaining tactical creativity, further increase in techno-tactical skills and perfection and automatization of favorite techno-tactical skills |
| Mental | Total commitment to excellence, attaining the highest level of self-confidence, self-regulation of mood , effective emotional control and mental toughness |

It is commonly agreed that outstanding athletes usually have striking and brilliant personalities. The individual traits of outstanding athletes have been subjected to thorough investigation.

**Studies**. Gould and others (2002) interviewed 10 Olympic champions and persons who knew them very well as for example, parents, coaches and colleagues. It was found that each outstanding athlete had the following personality traits: high level of confidence, optimism, adaptive perfectionism, sports intelligence and mental toughness. They had also the ability to cope with and control anxiety and to set and achieve real goals. The comparison of medal winning Olympians with less successful participants in the Olympic Games reveal additional important factors of sports excellence: the ability to react positively to unexpected events and numerous distractions, adhere to performance routines, team unity and cohesion, and support of family and friends (Gould & Carson, 2007).

In conclusion, it is worth noting that personality traits like confidence, optimism and sports intelligence, and factors such as social support, which contribute to an Olympians' success, are also relevant in early preparation, although to a lesser extent.

**4.4.2 Sensitive periods in the development of different motor abilities**

Both researchers and practitioners have remarked that during certain periods in an individuals life they are more trainable for certain motor abilities than in other times. These time periods have been termed "sensitive periods" and are based on the following physiological facts:

a) The natural development of physical (motor) abilities and physiological functions in children and youth is non-uniform. The sensitive periods make it possible to make more progress and have the most favorable rate of improvement in certain abilities;

b) The periods of acceleration and deceleration of motor development for different abilities do not coincide chronologically. Some of them occur earlier, others – later.

Non-uniformity and chronological heterogeneity in the development of various motor abilities are widely known phenomena. However, chronological determination of the sensitive periods with regard to specific motor abilities remains open to dispute. Each fitness component can be characterized by various indices, which can give different (and at times contradictory) chronological trends. This explains the variance in data from different sources. Other approaches entail comparing training-induced effects achieved at different ages. Using this approach, the sensitive periods were determined and are shown in Figure 4.9.

In general, the sensitive periods are determined by growth, maturation and natural trends in the development of the motor system. Physical activity and specially organized training are integrative factors that stimulate and augment the natural physical trend. For instance, the most favorable period for improvement of general motor coordination is between ages 9-12. Coordinated ability increases at an older age as well, but its improvement rate is lower. Similarly, flexibility increases considerably more at ages 7-10 when the high elasticity of tendons, ligaments and joints is beneficial for making progress. The elementary forms of speed also develop non-uniformly. The highest improvement rate for maximal movement speed occurs at ages 11-13 in both girls and boys while reaction time improves most at 9-11 years of age.

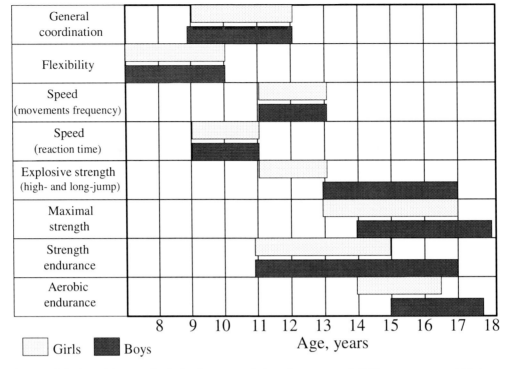

**Figure 4.9.** Sensitive periods in the natural development of different motor abilities (based on Meinel and Schnabel, 1976; Martin, 1980; Volkov, 1986)

The influence of growth and maturation is especially pronounced with regard to strength abilities. Achievements in the high- and long jump depends on powerful muscular contractions and body mass. The latter component increases most noticeably in mid-puberty girls aged 13-15; and their maximal improvement rate occurs at 11-13.

Boys perform better in the high- and long jumps at ages 13-17. The improvement in maximal strength attained in mid-puberty and late-puberty is directly affected by hormonal changes (maturation) and an increase in muscle mass (growth). It is well known that improvement in muscle strength is a result of better neural regulation as well as muscular hypertrophy. It is worth noting that training-induced hypertrophy is much more pronounced in adults in comparison to mid-pubertal or late-pubertal children. Therefore, improvement in neural regulation is the main source of increased explosive and maximal strength. Improvement in neural adaptation also contributes to gains in strength endurance. Other contributors relate to metabolic factors (aerobic and anaerobic energy supply) and hormonal aspects. More specifically, the androgenic hormones (e.g., testosterone) affect anaerobic power production and muscle hypertrophy but their concentration is low in children and only starts to increase at ages 12-13 in girls, and 13-14 in boys.

Practice has been shown to improve aerobic development greatly in children aged 9-12. However, the most favorable periods for aerobic endurance increases appear in mid-pubertal children, from age 14 in girls and 15 in boys. The most influential factors affecting this sensitive period are increased body size, and in particular, muscle mass, increased heart volume, total blood volume, and a higher hemoglobin concentration.

The sensitive periods are exploited in training systems with young athletes although commensurate pedagogical precautions are necessary. The higher sensitivity of children and youth can lead to overload and even injury. This is particularly relevant in training for maximum strength and in power exercises.

### 4.4.3 Identifying gifted athletes

In general, giftedness can be characterized as a predisposition to and a higher trainability for a given activity. These are considered to be genetically transmitted properties of an individual. In sports, properly developing giftedness implies attaining sports excellence. Apparently, the earlier this giftedness is identified, the more effectively the individual's athletic preparation can be managed and the greater is the probability of developing an elite athlete. Thus, a gifted child is potentially a talented athlete and, therefore, identification of giftedness can be based on unchangeable inherited predictors of talent.

According to the current approach (Williams & Franks, 1998; Williams & Reilly, 2000), sport talent is determined by four generalized factors: anthropometrical, physiological, psychological and sociological. Each of them contains numerous characteristics that can serve as predictors of potential talent. Some anthropometrical and physiological variables are highly dependent on heredity and as such, can not be compensated for by other personal traits. Thus, they can restrict progress in a given sport. Several psychological personality traits are somewhat inherited (Plomin et al., 1994; Saudino, 1997) and therefore can be altered during preparation. Sociological

153

conditions are not heredity-dependent. This doesn't mean, however, that they can be changed easily if necessary (Table 4.11).

**Table 4.11**

**Factors determining athletic talent, their characteristics and dependence on heredity**

| Factors | Characteristics | Genetic determination |
|---|---|---|
| Body build and body composition | Body height, extremity lengths and foot size | strong |
| | Shoulder width, thigh circumference, muscle mass | medium |
| | Total body fat | low |
| Physiological | Alactic Anaerobic Power Peak blood lactate Space orientation | high |
| | Glycolitic Anaerobic Power Strength endurance (resistance to acidity) Flexibility | medium |
| Psychological | Self-confidence Anxiety control Motivation Concentration | medium-low |
| Sociological | Parental support Socio-economic background Cultural background Coach-child interaction | heredity independent |

The identification of gifted, that is, potentially talented athletes, can be based on unchangeable predictors, most often associated with anthropometric and physiological factors. This approach led to the development of so-called model characteristics, which describe favorable combinations of anthropometric and physiological measurements for different age categories (Bulgakova, 1986). The characteristics were used for identifying candidates with the best prospects for benefiting from more specialized training. The main limitation of this evaluation is in the differing levels of maturity of children that are examined to determine giftedness. Children with slower rates of maturation may be found inferior to more mature teammates but may have greater potential for further progress.

154

Special attention should be given to determining the most favorable combinations of anthropometric and physiological estimates for different ages. Such age related models can be created through longitudinal study of a large group of athletes, where one sub-group attains the elite level. Data for the athletes recorded in the different periods can be used as model characteristics for corresponding age categories. It is obvious that such a study, which would take a number of years, appears difficult and has organizational problems, but such long-term research projects have been conducted (Vorontsov et al. 1999; Falk et al., 2003). Much more common are so-called cross-sectional studies that compare less successful and more successful youngsters. The results are used to reveal some specifics about hypothetically gifted athletes.

**Case study and example**. 320 swimmers aged 11-18, participated in the USA Select Program and were examined with respect to biological age, anthropometric status, muscle strength and power, swim-specific abilities and performance time. The results showed that the best athletes at younger ages are usually more mature than their less successful counterparts while the best athletes in the older ages are mostly on-time maturers (80% of the US National team) or late maturers (18% of the team). The authors suggest that high performing late maturers have better chances of remaining involved with the sport for longer periods (Troup et al., 1991)

Another approach to considering this problem is through retrospective studies, in which the development of outstanding athletes is carefully analyzed with respect to performance trend, changes in body size etc. The number of available characteristics for retrospective analysis is usually limited but the benefits of such studies are obvious since this is only way to reconstruct the unique progress of Olympic and world champions from childhood to the podium.

**Case study.** 35 world leading canoe-kayak paddlers who took part in the USSR National team and earned medals in the Olympic Games and World Championships within eight years prior to the study, were interviewed with respect to their official performance results from ages 14-15. This corresponded to the end of their first year of long-term preparation (respondents who began their preparation later were excluded from the analysis). The collected data were subjected to statistical analysis and the performance trends of elite paddlers were calculated (Figure 4.10). Despite the substantial improvement of paddles and boats in the two decades since this study was conducted, the results achieved by outstanding athletes in the earlier stages of their preparation remain relevant to this day for evaluation of giftedness in today's young athletes (Sozin, 1986).

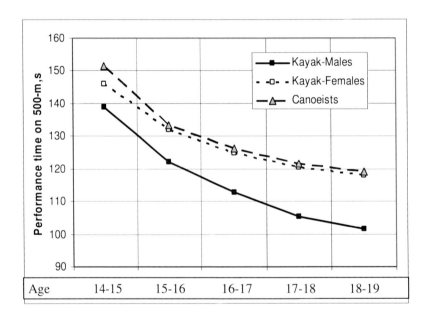

**Figure 4.10.** Performance times of extremely successful canoe-kayak paddlers that can be used for identifying giftedness in today's youngsters (adapted from Sozin, 1986)

In recent decades many research projects have been conducted in order to develop multidimensional models of gifted athletes in different sports. Such models encompass many characteristics of bodybuild, motor fitness etc. and make it possible to compare real children with virtual candidates for future excellence in a given sport.

See, for instance, the publications of Arnot & Gaines, 1986, and Brown, 2001, in which such data can be found.

Another general approach can be recommended to coaches in any of several sports as a part of the initial preparation of youngsters. This approach is based on the assumption that giftedness is comprised of two major components, a predisposition to a certain sport activity and trainability in related workloads (Figure 4.11). These components determine the effect of initial preparation. For example, a predisposition to a certain sport affects the *initial level* of relevant motor fitness (speed, endurance, agility etc.) while trainability, determines the development *improvement rate* during initial preparation. This assumption has several restrictions since a predisposition to a certain sport is not the only determining factor of the motor fitness level that can be examined. Previous experience in this activity (preliminary training, acquaintance with tests, etc.) also has a strong effect on the outcome of the initial tests.

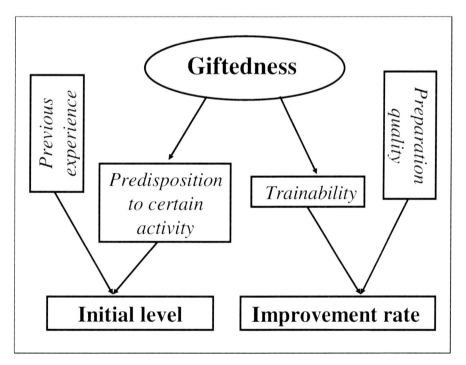

**Figure 4.11.** Giftedness as a general but not the only factor determining the initial level and improvement rate during beginning athletic preparation

**Example**. Examine the swimming fitness of a group of eight year old children. A few members of the group already have some aquatic experience (practice with parents or older relatives, games in shallow water etc.), others have had a few lessons and are more or less accustomed to movement in water, and the rest have no experience at all. Because of this, the behavior of these children in water will be very different and previous experiences will affect the results much more strongly than the children's real predisposition to competitive swimming.

The second problem relates to the improvement rate during initial preparation that depends not only on an individual's trainability but also on the quality of the preparation. This becomes evident when comparing the progress of athletes who train under different conditions with different coaches. However, for athletes training in one group with the same coach, improvement rate adequately reflects trainability.

Based on this so-called dual approach to giftedness, identification is limited to evaluation of the initial level of sport-specific fitness and its improvement rate during initial preparation. This method of diagnosis was first implemented in team and dual sports mostly because of practical needs (Bril, 1980). The general logic of the dual approach is presented in Figure 4.12.

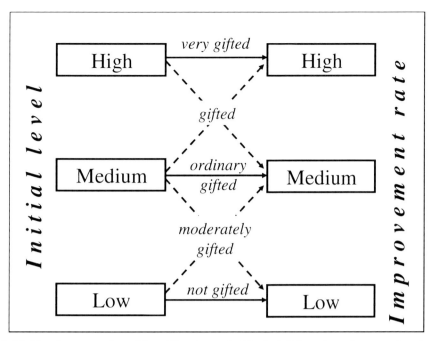

**Figure 4.12.** Dual approach to identification of gifted children based on evaluation of the initial level of sport-specific fitness and its improvement rate during initial preparation (based on Bril, 1980, and the author's modifications)

One more remark must be made concerning the optimal duration of preparation necessary to evaluate improvement rate, i.e., the trainability of young athletes. There is no simple unequivocal answer to this question since the following circumstances must be considered:

1) The absolute unsuitability of certain individuals for specific sports can be recognized quickly (tall and heavy candidates in gymnastics; small children in basketball etc.);

2) Non-gifted candidates can usually be recognized during short-term preliminary preparation lasting about three-four months;

3) Diagnosing giftedness in maximal speed and power sports needs a relatively short period and usually lasts up to one year;

4) Identification of gifted children in highly coordinated sports (gymnastics, figure skating etc.) is limited by the initial preparation, which is usually earlier than in other sports (Figure 4.8). Also, the evaluation process takes between 1-2 years;

5) In team and dual sports, where children start systematic preparation relatively later (Figure 7.8), very gifted athletes can be identified faster (two-three months) but this process usually takes about one year;

6) Perhaps the longest period for giftedness identification is needed in endurance sports, where many world-level athletes are recognized as potential elite athletes after three-four years of systematic preparation.

---

**Evidence of genetics**. Based on the outcomes of studies with young adult twins, it has been found that the contribution of heredity related factors to training response in an endurance program is different for earlier and later stages of preparation. The initial preparation is less dependent on heredity. However, as athletes progress and approach higher workloads, the genetic control of their training response becomes much stronger (Bouchard et al., 2000). This characteristic of training responses partly explains why some gifted endurance athletes cannot be effectively recognized at an earlier stage of their preparation.

---

A final remark relates to the genetic component of athletic giftedness that cannot be underestimated. It relates to a coach's interest in the athletic history of the family and the achievements of the older relatives that is both reasonable and desirable. Only a few outstanding athletes had great champions among their parents. Most of them were born and grew up in families with physically active and sport oriented persons.

**Summary**

Long-term athletic preparation has been considered with respect to designing relatively prolonged training cycles (annual and quadrennial), multi-year preparation of adult, and multi-year preparation of young athletes. The basics of annual cycle construction included goals and objectives, sequencing the main steps in the annual plan, and general tendencies in workload compilation. All these items are considered in light of the Block Periodization concept.

Special attention was given to seasonal trends in training workloads within the annual cycle of preparation (Table 4.3). Particulars regarding quadrennial planning were given for preparing highly qualified athletes. Special attention was given to workload trends in preparing older and experienced athletes and their younger counterparts. Also, the problem of athletic longevity was briefly analyzed with respect to the characteristics of the older experienced athletes (Table 4.5).

The typical trend in annual training workloads was presented together with a case study of many-time world and Olympic canoeing champion Ivan Klementiev (Latvia), while physiological changes during long-term preparation were considered on the basis of a case study of World Champion and seven-time Tour de France champion, Lance Armstrong (USA). It was seen that many older athletes approach their biological limits but continue to attain outstanding performances, and even improve their athletic results. The source of such individual progress can be attributed to better utilization of their motor and physiological capabilities, where individual creativity, self-confidence and athletic wisdom play a big role.

The common approach to long-term athletic preparation assumes there are four separate stages. They are preliminary preparation, initial specialization, advanced specialization, and sports perfection. Each of these is characterized by the proper combination of stage length, frequency and duration of workouts, yearly training volume and other sport-specific variables. The physical, technical, tactical and mental characteristics of each stage were summarized and considered in general (Tables 4.7-4.10).

In terms of biological maturation, the concept of sensitive periods is of special importance. It assumes there are the periods in an individuals life when they are more trainable for certain motor abilities than at other times. Consequently, the periods of most favorable training responses can be exploited for more conscientious and beneficial development (Figure 4.9). Special attention was given to the identification of gifted young athletes, because early identification of giftedness permits more effective management of preparation in talented athletes with great potential. Prospective and retrospective approaches for determining valid and informative indicators of giftedness were considered. For practical purposes and general evaluation of giftedness, it is highly recommended that the initial level of sport-specific fitness characteristics be evaluated as a predisposition to a given sport. The improvement rate of athletic abilities during initial preparation should be evaluated as an indicator of trainability. The comprehensive scheme presented in Figure 4.12 makes it possible to estimate athletic giftedness in general.

**References for Chapter 4**

Arnot, A.,Gaines, Ch. (1986). *Sports talent*. N.Y.: Penguin Books

Arkajev, L., Suchilin, N. (2004). How to prepare champions. Theory and technology of preparation the highly qualified gymnasts. Moscow: Fizkultura i sport

Armstrong, L. (2000). It's not about the bike. New York: Putman

Bouchard, C., Wolfarth, B., Rivera, M.A. et al., (2000). Genetic determinants of endurance performance. . In: Shephard R.J. & Astrand P.-O.(ed.). *Endurance in Sport. Vol.II of the Encyclopedia of Sports Medicine*. 2nd edition. Oxford: Blackwell Science, p. 223-244.

Bril, M. (1980). *Selection in ball games*. Moscow: Fizkultura i sport.

Brown, J. (2001). *Sports talent. How to identify and develop outstanding athletes*. Champaign, IL: Human Kinetics.

Bulgakova, N. (1986). *Selection and preparation of young swimmers*. Moscow: Fizkultura i sport:

Coyle, E. (2005). Improved muscular efficiency displayed as Tour de France champion matures. *J Appl Physiol*. 98:2191-2196.

Falk, B., Lidor, R., Lander, Y. et al., (2003). Talent identification and early development of the elite water-polo players : a 2-year follow-up study. *J Sports Sciences*, 22:347-355.

Gould, D.,Carson, S. (2007). Psychological preparation in sport. In: Blumenshtein B., Lidor R., and Tenenbaum G.(Eds.). *Psychology of Sport Training*. Oxford: Mayer & Mayer Sport Ltd., p. 115-136.

Issurin,V. (1994). General concept of preparing young kayakers. In: Issurin, V. and Dotan, R. (Eds.). *The science and practice of training junior kayak/canoe paddlers*. Proceedings of the International Seminar on Kayak. Israel. p. 7-22.

Klementiev, I. (1994). Long-term preparation from the beginner to the champion level. In: Issurin, V. and Dotan, R. (Eds.) *The science and practice of training junior kayak/canoe paddlers*. Proceedings of the International Seminar on Kayak. Israel.
p.85-100.

Martin, D. (1980). *Grundlagen der Trainingslehre*. Schorndorf: Verlag Karl Hoffmann.

Meinel, K., Schnabel, G. (1976). *Bewegungslehre*. Berlin: Volk und Wissen.

Padilla, S., Mujika, I., Angulo, F. and Goiriena, J. (2000). Scientific approach to the 1-h cycling world record: a case study. *J Appl Physiol.* 89:1522-1527.

Platonov, V., Sakhnovsky, K. (1988). *Preparation of young athlete.* Kiev: "Radianska shkola".

Plomin, R., Owen, M.J. and McGuffin, P. (1994). The genetic basis of complex human behaviors. *Scienc*e, 264, 1733-1739.

Saudino, K.J. (1997). Moving beyond heritability questions: New directions in behaviorial genetic studies of personality. *Current Directives in Psychological Science,* 4, 86-90.

Sozin,Y. (1986). *Selection of canoe-kayak paddlers within different stages of long-term preparation.* Thesis of Ph.D. dissertation. Kiev: State Sport University.

Troup et al., (1991). Growth and developmental changes of the age-group swimmers. In: *Studies by the International Center for Aquatic Research.* Colorado Springs: US Swimming Press, p.25-33.

Volkov, N. (1986). Biochemistry of sport. In: Menshikov V. and Volkov, N. (Eds.), *Biochemistry.* Moscow: Fizkultura i sport, p.267-381.

Vorontsov A.R., Dyrco V.V., Binevsky D.A. et al. (1999). Patterns of growth for some characteristics of physical development, functional and motor abilities in boy-swimmers 11-18 years. In: Keskinen, K., Komi, P. and Hollander, P. (Eds.). *Biomechanics and Medicine in Swimming VIII.*University of Jyvaskula, Finland, pp.327-334.

Williams, A., Franks, A. (1998). Talent identification in soccer. Sports. *Exercise and Injury,* 4, 159-165.

Williams & Reilly, (2000). Talent identification and development in soccer. *J Sports Sciences,* 18: 657-667.

Yessis, M., (2006). *Build a Better Athlete.* Terre Haute, IN: Equilibrium Books

# Chapter 5

Oreste Perri

Two-time world champion, personal coach of a number of Olympic champions,

Head coach of Italian canoe-kayak national team

# Chapter 5

# Altitude training

Altitude training has been a greatly disputed topic in sports science and of much interest to researchers and coaches for over three decades. Generally speaking, the present situation is paradoxical. Publications written for coaches consider altitude training to be an efficacious and proven tool for enhancing high-level performance (Fuchs & Reiss, 1990; Dick, 1992; Suslov et al., 1999) while exercise physiology textbooks and professional reviews state that altitude training provides no extra benefits for sea level performance than conventional training (Jensen & Fisher,1979; McArdle et al., 1991; Wilmore & Costill, 1993; Saltin, 1996, inter alia).

From a practical viewpoint, the positive experiences of prominent coaches, great athletes and several national teams, offer strong arguments for employing altitude training. Many successful national teams, particularly in the endurance sports, incorporate altitude training as part of their preparation. This chapter summarizes the current body of physiological and methodological data concerning altitude training with respect to training program design. The scientific background presented here is limited and readers are advised to refer to other sources (see reviews of Boning et al., 1997; Rusko et al., 2004; Wilber, 2004 and others).

## 5.1. Scientific background

As is well known, sport related scientific studies were initiated as a result of world-level competitions at altitude: the 1955 Pan-American Games held in Mexico City (elevation 2200-2300m); the 1960 Winter Olympic Games in Squaw Valley (elevation 2000m); and in particular, the 1968 Summer Olympic Games in Mexico City. At that time, earlier studies and pilot investigations concentrated on elaborate training programs at altitude in order to succeed in altitude performances. Later, when the basic knowledge had been accumulated and various altitude training facilities became available, training at altitude to enhance performance at sea-level was introduced. Since then, the amount of scientific information on altitude training has constantly increased. Some of the relevant data are reviewed below.

### 5.1.1. General factors affecting altitude performance

Two general factors affect athletic performance at altitude, aerodynamics and physiology. As is well known, sea level air density diminishes with increased altitude. Thus, air density at 2300m (the altitude of Mexico City) is about 20% less than at sea level. Certainly, the reduction of air density and the corresponding decrease in aerodynamic resistance allow higher velocities to be attained. The results of the Mexico City Olympics in sprint events were related to this theoretical position. Winning Olympic sprinters attained their personal best results in spite of the more difficult physiological conditions of performance. In addition, Bob Beamon's new Olympic and world record for the long jump bettered the previous one by 55cm (!) – an unheard of accomplishment.

Unlike the aerodynamic factor, the physiological impact of altitude is very negative, mainly because of the decreased partial pressure of oxygen in ambient air. This lower oxygen content immediately reduces the athletes' aerobic abilities during the initial period of altitude acclimatization. The general explanation for this is that the decreased oxygen content in the atmosphere reduces oxygen blood saturation and delivery to the muscle cells. Hence, in the long distance events, where oxygen supply

166

is of great importance, athletic performance tends to decrease. This was clearly demonstrated by the results in the Mexico City Olympics (Figure 5.1).

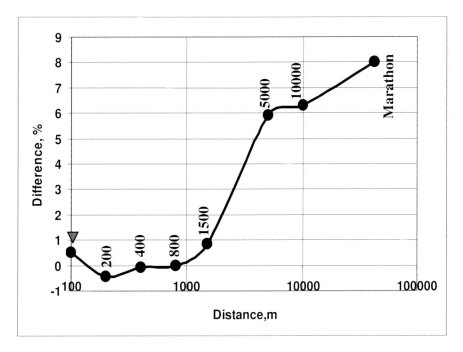

**Figure 5.1.** Difference between winning results at the 1968 Mexico City Olympics and current world records in various running events (based on data published by Wilber, 2004)

▼- At that time the world record was hand-timed while the Olympic performance was done electronically

The above graph clearly shows the advantageous zone – sprints including the long and triple jumps, and the disadvantageous zone – endurance events, where performance decreased as distance increased. Of course, adaptation to altitude conditions was extremely important in medium- and long-duration events. Residents and especially natives living at high altitude, enjoy big benefits in terms of oxygen delivery and utilization. It is noteworthy that in the Mexico City Olympics, the gold and silver medals in the 5000m, 10000m, marathon and 3000m steeplechase events were won by natives of high altitude countries: Ethiopia, Kenya, and Tunisia. It was obvious, even before the Mexico City Olympics, that altitude performances aside from the short-duration events, require preliminary altitude training. However, after these Olympics both scientists and coaches focused their attention on another problem, how to better employ altitude training in preparing athletes for sea level performances.

### 5.1.2. Basics of altitude adaptation

Besides reduced air density and decreased oxygen content in ambient air, a number of environmental factors affect athletes' responses at altitude, namely: increased sun and ultra-violet radiation, reduced temperatures and humidity, delightful landscapes and mountainous beauty. Traditionally, consideration of altitude exposure and training is focused on the hypoxia factor, but in fact, many environmental factors are also at play and help determine the athletes' response. It is known that significant effects from altitude exposure start at an elevation of 1600m, and altitudes higher than 2600m are usually not used for training camps.

The responses that occur during initial exposure are acute responses lasting from a few hours to a few days, and long-term responses that last two-five weeks or even more (Table 5.1).

Examination of the physiological changes induced by exposure to and training at medium level altitude shows that arrival at altitude and breathing air with lower oxygen content causes an excitation of chemoreceptors and a reflexive increase in pulmonary ventilation. This increase is a compensatory mechanism to bring the same amount of oxygen into the lungs as at sea level. Such hyperventilation occurs both at rest and during exercise. The blood plasma volume decreases immediately after arrival at altitude. After a week or more it returns to pre-altitude levels and even increases above sea-level values (Saltin, 1996). Heart rate at rest and during moderate workloads increases proportionally to the decrease of partial pressure of oxygen. An additional reason for the heart rate increase could be catecholamine excretion (mostly adrenalin) that occurs in particular at initial exposure.

**Table 5.1**

**Acute and long-term responses of athletes to altitude exposure and training**

(based on McArdle et al., 1991; Brooks et al., 1996; Wilber, 2004)

| Physiological functions | Acute responses | Long-term responses |
|---|---|---|
| Pulmonary ventilation | Increased pulmonary ventilation due to reduced oxygen content | Pulmonary ventilation remains increased |
| Heart rate | Increased heart rate at rest and during exercise, decreased maximal heart rate | Return of heart rate to pre-altitude level, maximum heart rate remains decreased |
| Stroke volume | Reduced stroke volume at rest and during intense exercise | Return of stroke volume to pre-altitude levels |
| Cardiac output | Reduced cardiac output at rest and during intense exercise | Return of cardiac output to pre-altitude levels |
| Blood lactate | Increased lactate accumulation after intense and maximal exercise | Decreased lactate values after intense and maximal exercise in comparison to pre-altitude levels |
| Aerobic energy supply | Reduction of maximal oxygen uptake by 1% for each 100m of altitude elevation | Increase in aerobic enzymes, return of maximum oxygen uptake to near pre-altitude levels |
| Anaerobic capacity | Hypoxia accelerates glycolitic reactions and glycogenolysis | Increased muscle buffering increases anaerobic capacity |
| Hormone regulation | Increased catecholamine level, release of erythropoietin that stimulates production of erythrocytes and hemoglobin | Increased cortisol that indicates a stress reaction and affects muscle catabolism |
| Hematological responses | Plasma volume and total blood volume decrease immediately after arrival | Increased total blood volume, number of erythrocytes and amount of hemoglobin |
| Skeletal muscles | | Increased capillary density, possible muscle mass decrease due to cortisol catabolic action |
| Fluid balance | Tendency toward dehydration due to increased respiratory and urinary water loss | Increased fluid intake can be as much as four-five liters per day |
| Immune system | Increased risk of upper body respiratory infections | Increased level of stress hormones (catecholamines, cortisol) that suppress immune function |

Stroke volume at rest and during moderate and high intensity workloads, decreases substantially within the initial two days. After a number of days stroke volume returns to pre-attitude levels. Nevertheless, heart rate increases markedly, and cardiac output remains decreased at rest and during various workloads for several days (Wilber, 2004).

One of the important outcomes of hypoxia is reduction of kidney oxygenation that stimulates synthesis of erythropoietin (EPO), a hormone that regulates production of erythrocytes and hemoglobin. The increased concentration of EPO elicits synthesis of additional erythrocytes and hemoglobin, a process that takes approximately five-seven days. After that, the oxygen carrying capacity of the blood increases markedly as does aerobic ability. These changes explain the dramatic reduction of maximal oxygen uptake during acute exposure and its gradual increase during acclimatization. In the initial days, the hypoxic environment accelerates glycolitic reactions and glycogen breakdown. At this time anaerobic threshold decreases dramatically and corresponding speed regimes decrease as well. In line with these changes, the metabolic response to habitual exercise also changes. As athletes approach their previously comfortable speed regime there is a sharp increase in blood lactate. Further acclimatization follows to increase muscle buffering capacity that prevents excessive acidosis (pH reduction) during severe workloads.

Serious altitude training for a week or a little more, leads to increased secretion of cortisol that stimulates catabolic reactions and possible reduction of muscle mass. Indeed, remarkable decreases in muscle mass and body weight have been noted among top-level athletes (Issurin, Kaverin, 1990). Another consequence of increased cortisol is suppression of the immune function with an increased risk of upper respiratory infections, a concern for sport physicians. Immediately after arrival at altitude increased respiratory and urinary loss of water may cause dehydration. Therefore, during the entire altitude exposure, fluid intake should be increased by four-five liters per day.

For a long time, the potential benefits of altitude training were associated with hematological changes, i.e., increased oxygen delivery to muscles. In fact these changes are transient and very soon erythrocytes and hemoglobin return to pre-altitude levels after returning at sea level (a few days to one week). Another contributor to the post-altitude ergogenic effect is enhancement of anaerobic abilities due to the increased buffering capacity of muscles and blood. Additionally, there may be enhanced cellular adaptation of muscles. This factor has been studied less and is rarely considered. Nevertheless, it is known that training at altitude (or altitude-simulated conditions) leads to increased muscle capillarity, which facilitates oxygen extraction from the blood (Mizuno et al., 1990). Other favorable changes can also occur in the muscle microstructure (Terrados et al., 1990).

---

**Study and example**. Ten male subjects trained for four weeks on a cycle-ergometer with one leg. The training protocol consisted of exercising one leg under normobaric (sea-level) conditions, and another leg under hypoxic conditions corresponding to an altitude of 2300 m. The test battery included endurance trials and needle biopsy with subsequent evaluation of muscle enzymes and myoglobin in the extracted sample. Comparison of the altitude-trained leg with the non-altitude trained one allowed researchers to assess the effect of altitude-simulated training. It resulted in significantly superior endurance, significantly increased activity of oxidative enzymes and a higher concentration of myoglobin (Terrados et al., 1990).

---

In summary, even a simplified consideration of acute and long-term responses to altitude exposure indicates many difficulties related to the athletes' preparation. The potential benefits still look complicated and dubious.

## 5.1.3. Does altitude training provide benefits?

Although this question is not relevant for many coaches, it remains very tangible for many physiologists. Generally speaking, the existing situation is paradoxical since exercise physiology textbooks state that altitude training provides no benefits for sea level performance in comparison to appropriate training at sea level (Jensen & Fisher,1979: McArdle et al., 1991; Wilmore & Costill, 1993; Brooks et al., 1996). Nevertheless, the number of athletes practicing at altitude camps, as well as the number of altitude training centers, is constantly increasing. Many great athletes from different sports like Alexander Popov (swimming) and Lance Armstrong (cycling) systematically used altitude camps. Frederick (1974) showed that all gold medals in the running events, from 1500m through the marathon at the

1972 Munich Olympics, were won by athletes who used altitude training. Despite the scientific contradictions and theoretical disputes, altitude training has become a component of the preparatory program among many successful national teams.

**Case study**. During the 1999 European swimming championship, the head coaches of leading national teams (Germany, Great Britain, France, Italy, Russia, Spain and Sweden) were questioned by this author on the use of altitude training. All respondents reported that their teams practiced in altitude training camps as part of their annual preparation. However, each of them noted that several athletes, usually the older and more experienced members of the team, did not take part in altitude camps. The reasons offered by the different coaches were very similar – an unfavorable response by the athletes to altitude training

The above example demonstrates that prominent coaches, supported by qualified sport experts and physicians, make a conscious choice to incorporate altitude training in their preparatory programs. It is hard to imagine that they didn't find sufficient arguments for incorporating altitude training programs over the decades. However, not all members of a national team participated in the altitude program. Exceptions were noted in each team. The coaches resolved the problem by dividing athletes into "responders" and "non-responders" and then releasing the latter from altitude programs. This practical approach is consistent with scientific data showing that "responders" and "non-responders" are recognizable on the basis of hematological responses and rate of performance gains (Chapman et al., 1998). Additional support of this concept can be found in human genetics studies.

**Genetic evidence**. Scientists have long investigated common genetic markers to determine whether there are differences in the frequency of genotypes between top-level athletes and control populations (de Garay et al., 1974). The 14th human chromosome was found to contain the so-called Hypoxia-Inducible Factor 1α that serves as a genetic regulator of EPO synthesis and release during altitude exposure and training (Vogt et al., 2001; Wilber, 2004). Athletes with a genetic predisposition to a favorable response to hypoxia, release much higher concentrations of EPO at altitude (Witkovski et al., 2002). Apparently these athletes manifest beneficial hematological changes induced by altitude training.

It should be noted that investigation of altitude training effects have resulted in very different outcomes. Several research groups found no post-altitude improvement in physiological variables (hematological changes, maximal oxygen consumption) or in athletic performance (Hahn et al., 1992; Telford et al., 1996; Balley et al., 1998). Other studies reported significant gains both in maximal oxygen consumption and athletic performance (Chung et al., 1995; Levine & Stray-Gundersen, 1997). These contradictions can be partly explained by the "responders vs. non-responders" concept. From this viewpoint it is interesting to consider the findings, which were obtained in a group consisting of "responders" only.

**Study and example**. Seven highly qualified middle- and long-distance runners underwent a three week training camp at altitude (1850 m). Each of them systematically used altitude training over a number of years and their positive responses were confirmed by distinct performance gains. Maximal oxygen consumption was determined prior to altitude camp and on the third week of sea level re-acclimatization (Figure 5.2). All runners improved their pre-altitude aerobic ability and the average gain for the entire group was significant ($P<0.05$): 7.4% (Suslov et al., 1999).

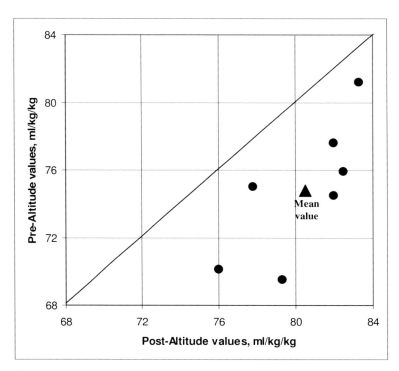

**Figure** 5.**2.** Gain in maximum oxygen consumption after three weeks of
altitude training in a group of highly qualified middle- and
long-distance runners (based on Suslov et al., 1999).

Summarizing the preceding section, it can be said that athletes belonging to
the "responders" category can benefit from well designed altitude training. The
physiological factors that contribute to the so-called the post-altitude ergogenic effect
can be found in a review of current world literature. There are three potential benefits
of altitude training (Table 5.2).

**Table** 5.2

**Potential benefits of altitude training on performance**

**enhancement at sea level**

| Potential benefits | Comments | Sources |
|---|---|---|
| Improved oxygen delivery to muscles | Lower oxygen in ambient air elicits a synthesis of the hormone erythropoietin (EPO) that stimulates production of additional red blood cells and hemoglobin, which in turn provide greater delivery of oxygen to the muscles. In addition, total blood volume increases | Saltin.,1996; Ekblom & Berglund, 1991 |
| Enhanced oxygen utilization within the muscle cells | Altitude training increases the concentration of myoglobin, the activity of aerobic enzymes and number of mitochondria, and muscle capillarization increases as well | Terrados et al.,1988,1990 ; Mizuno et al., 1990 |
| Increased anaerobic capacity via improved buffering in muscles and blood | Altitude training increases the ability of blood and muscles to buffer the concentration of hydrogen ions and prevent excessive acidosis; as a result, athletes' anaerobic capacity increases | Mizuno et al., 1990 ; Gore et al., 2001 |

Further consideration of the benefits listed requires some critical evaluation. Increased erythrocyte numbers and hemoglobin mass fall quickly after returning to sea-level (Wilmore & Costill, 1993), although larger blood volume takes 2-4 weeks before it gradually normalizes (Saltin, 1996). It has been suggested that the blood of some athletes retains increased oxygen carrying capacity for longer periods while in other athletes this benefit is lost faster. Improved cellular adaptation of muscles caused by altitude training appears to have potential benefits but at present there is little to support this hypothesis. Increased anaerobic capacity seems to be a benefit for sea level performance as it helps explain why many top-level sprinters (400 m runners, 100 m swimmers, etc.) have continued to use altitude training camps over the last three decades.

## 5.2. Training fundamentals

Apparently, the physiological responses to altitude training are very different from training at sea level. Consequently, training programs at altitude should reflect these differences. They must correspond to physiological demands and not exceed the limits of biological adaptation. However, they should also produce the planned for cumulative training effect. Therefore, appropriate general principles, basic methodology and practical guidelines are required. They are presented below.

### 5.2.1. General principles and basic positions of altitude training

The following four general principles are of primary importance in training and coaching.

1)      The general goal. One of three options should be selected:
   - Is altitude training intended to prepare athletes for altitude performance?
   - Is altitude training supposed to exploit post-altitude effects in sea level competitions?
   - Is altitude training intended to diversify and activate annual preparation?

2)      Selecting the athletes who respond positively to altitude training.
   The decision to include an athlete in the altitude program should be made with respect to his/her individual responses, previous altitude experience and data from relevant medical examinations.

3)      Structuring the training program according to phases of altitude acclimatization. Pre-altitude training, altitude conditions (elevation, climate, weather etc.) and individual particulars of the athletes (previous experience at altitude, age, bodyweight and muscle mass, aerobic capacity etc.) affect the duration of each phase.

4)      Structuring the post-altitude training program with respect to phases of sea level re-acclimatization. This principle also involves participation in competition and the utilization of the post-altitude ergogenic effect.

The first principle relates to preparation strategy when coaches and sport administrators decide to incorporate altitude training. There are at least three general purposes of altitude training and each of them determines the proper features of annual preparation (Table 5.3).

**Table 5.3**

**Purposes and general features of altitude training in the athletes' annual preparation cycle**

| Purpose of altitude training | Types of mesocycles employed | Number of altitude camps | Total altitude exposure |
|---|---|---|---|
| Preparation for sea level performance | Accumulation Transmutation | Two-three | 35-60 days |
| Preparation for altitude performance | Accumulation Transmutation Realization | Three-four | 50-100 days |
| Diversification and improvement of annual preparation | Accumulation | One-two | 15-25 days |

The use of altitude training for improving sea level performance assumes several physiological benefits considered previously (Table 5.2). From both the physiological and methodological points of view, it is important to individually check the athlete's responses and adapt him/her to unusual workloads and reactions in advance. It can be hypothesized that utilizing physiological benefits provides definite and predictable training responses in repeated altitude camps. In any case, the training used to exploit the post-altitude effect, which were developed in the USSR (Suslov, 1983) and the GDR (Reiss, 1988), entailed strict adherence to two or three repeated altitude camps.

The second principle refers to the concept of "responders" and "non-responders" (Chapman et al., 1998). This differentiation can be made by using objective scientific methods or with the help of practical sport-specific indicators. In any case, evaluation requires one-two altitude camps where individual training responses can be checked. Practical experience shows that the majority of high-level athletes, particularly in endurance sports, respond positively to altitude training. Nevertheless, even among responders the variability of individual reactions is very high.

The most influential factor in adaptation is the accumulated experience from previous camps. It has been noted that athletes with more experience at altitude overcome initial acclimatization problems better and faster. This accelerated adaptation is achieved because of physiological factors such as more favorable hormonal reactions, better hematological response, etc. and more effective behavior during training and restoration. During the first camp young athletes (18-21 yr) usually respond more beneficially. Additional advantages in initial adaptation include smaller muscle mass and higher aerobic capacity, which usually creates more economical and favorable responses.

The third and fourth principles require special considerations that are presented in sections 5.2.2 and 5.2.3. First, additional remarks are needed with regard to the usefulness of altitude training in different sports and the employment of altitude training as part of Block Periodization.

Traditionally, altitude training has been considered especially suitable for the endurance sports (Saltin, 1996; Reiss, 1998; Rusko, 2004). However, the spectrum of sports for which altitude training has been used is much wider. Objectives such as active recovery and general conditioning make reasonable use of altitude training in any sport. For instance, Soviet astronauts systematically used training camps in the altitude athletic center in Armenia. Athletes from combat and team and dual sports used altitude training to improve general and sport-specific endurance. In addition, potential benefits like enhanced anaerobic capacity (Table 5.2) can provide better speed endurance which expands the range of athletic events for which altitude training is applicable. The power sports are also thought to benefit from altitude training (Suslov et al., 1999) as the positive effects relate mostly to general environmental factors and breaking the routine of habitual workouts. Nevertheless, the largest group of altitude training proponents is formed by the endurance sports where the amount of scientific and empirical findings is extremely great.

It should be emphasized that many years before the first publications about Block Periodization appeared, the idea of highly concentrated workloads directed at developing a minimal number of motor abilities was proposed with regard to altitude training. These altitude mesocycles were termed "blocks of aerobic workloads at altitude". Coaches creatively combined these blocks with subsequent mesocycles having highly intense workloads in a manner very similar to the contemporary practice of Block Periodization. The most widely used mesocycle at altitude is accumulation. More prolonged exposure at altitude makes it possible to conduct a part or even an entire transmutation mesocycle.  In very special cases, in preparation for altitude performance, the realization mesocycle precedes competition (Table 5.4).

**Table 5.4**

**Proposed workloads and types of mesocycles used at altitude training**

| Proposed workloads | Type of mesocycle | Comments |
|---|---|---|
| General conditioning, low and moderate intensity aerobic workloads, use of semi-specific training means | Accumulation | Intended mostly for the early season |
| Anaerobic threshold exercises, maximum strength or aerobic strength endurance workloads and the use of alactic bouts | Accumulation | Intended mainly for the mid season |
| Aerobic-anaerobic endurance and anaerobic glycolitic sport-specific exercises, anaerobic strength endurance workloads | Transmutation | Can be used only after sufficient acclimatization |
| General conditioning and sport-specific aerobic programs intended to activate preparation for the target competition | Accumulation | Planned as the initial part of Final Stage Preparation |
| Pre-competitive taper, event-specific simulation and maximal speed exercises combined with full recovery | Realization | Can be used prior to competition at altitude |

### 5.2.2. Phases of altitude acclimatization and training program design

Altitude acclimatization is a highly complex process that is affected by environmental and physiological factors, training methodology and individual factors. Despite the complexity of this process and variety of individual responses, three separate phases of acclimatization can be pinpointed (Table 5.5).

# Table 5.5
## Phases of altitude acclimatization and their general characteristics
## (Issurin & Vrijens, 1995)

| Phases | General Characteristics | Duration |
|---|---|---|
| Acute | Increased heart rate at rest and during exercise<br>Substantially reduced speed at anaerobic threshold<br>Increased lactate accumulation during moderate intensity exercise<br>Increased pulmonary ventilation | 3-7 days |
| Transition | Normalized reaction to exercise with low and moderate intensity<br>Increased heart rate and lactate accumulation during intense exercise<br>Slightly reduced speed at anaerobic threshold<br>Increased pulmonary ventilation | 3-5 days |
| Stabilization | Normalized reaction to exercise with low, moderate and high intensity<br>Normalized lactate accumulation with intense exercise<br>Speed at anaerobic threshold approaches pre-altitude level<br>Increased erythrocytes and hemoglobin mass | Rest |

The acute phase of acclimatization is most restricted in terms of training capacity. For inexperienced athletes, this period can elicit poor behavior reactions as for example, when excited athletes show excessive effort and provoke exaggerated responses. These disorders can be associated with increased catecholamine secretion and reduced self-control. The duration of this phase depends on the individual traits of each athlete but is usually shorter for athletes who have experienced a number of altitude camps.

The transition phase is characterized by more favorable but unstable and less predictable responses. In this phase, the athlete can feel excessive fatigue after a relatively small load and movement technique may become less controlled. The duration of this phase varies according to the individual. Also, the period during which athletes must train at reduced workloads varies from 6-12 days. Precautions are necessary when using highly intense glycolitic exercises since employing them prematurely may adversely affect the athletes' adaptation. When the stabilization phase is established, athletes are able to execute large workloads almost without limitation (Table 5.6).

**Table 5.6**

**General approach to structuring a training program according to phases of altitude acclimatization (Issurin & Vrijens, 1995)**

| Characteristics of training | Acute phase | Transitional phase | Stabilization phase |
|---|---|---|---|
| Type of microcycle | Adjustment | Loading | Loading and/or impact |
| Duration of microcycle | 3-7 days | 3-5 days | 5-7 days |
| Number of microcycles | One | One | One - three |
| Total volume of exercise | Normal or 10-20% less | Normal or 5-10% less | Normal |
| Volume of exercise with higher intensity | 40-60% less | 15-30% less | Normal |
| Coordination complexity | Lower | Slightly lower | Normal |

As shown in Table 5.6 the initial microcycle program greatly differs from the pre-altitude standard. Attempts to start an altitude program with the usual training regimes used at sea level have been made in various sports resulting in the athletes inability to sustain the training program in the next microcycle. As a rule, such athletes did not succeed in the re-acclimatization period and did not improve their sea level performance. Thus, the initial microcycle performed with a slightly reduced total exercise volume, should exploit more economical workloads of reduced intensity and lower coordination complexity.

During the transition phase, exercise volume achieves its normal level but exercise intensity still remains lower. The stabilization phase allows, and even requires, the use of large workloads which ultimately determine the cumulative and residual effects of the altitude program. This high workload level is sustained almost until the end of altitude camp. Nevertheless, during the last one-two days workload levels should be reduced in order to facilitate the initial re-acclimatization at sea level.

The last aspect concerns the duration of the altitude training camp. The general approach to determining the required duration of altitude exposure is presented in Figure 5.3.

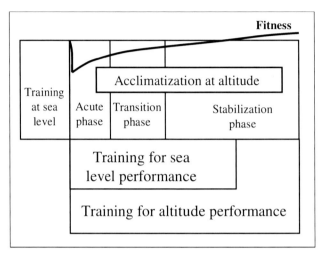

**Figure** 5.**3.** Duration of altitude camp when training is intended for sea level or altitude performance (based on Issurin & Vrijens, 1995)

If the training is intended to ensure success in altitude competition, the effect of altitude camp will be determined mainly by the gain in the preparedness attained in the stabilization phase. Consequently, it is reasonable to prolong work in this phase up to three or even four weeks. In this case, the total duration of altitude camp can be one month or more. If the program is intended to prepare athletes for sea level competition, its purpose is to attain a sufficient level of physiological adaptation. Thus, the camp duration can vary from 20-25 days, which corresponds to recommendations given by several training experts (Suslov, 1983; Fuchs & Reiss, 1990).

In conclusion, two typical mistakes can be noted:

- Ignoring altitude specificity (or not giving it sufficient attention) when designing the training program and,
- Forgoing strenuous workloads when athletes are already adapted to altitude conditions.

### 5.2.3. Post-altitude re-acclimatization and athletic performance

The state of the capacity and sport-specific performance athlete training during the period of re-acclimatization varies widely and is determined by at least three factors:
- phases of fitness and physiological changes during this period;
- workload deviations during post-altitude training;
- individual traits of athletes.

Periodic deviations in maximal performance and the physiological state during post-altitude re-acclimatization were found and analyzed (Table 5.7).

**Table 5.7**

**Periodic deviations of the athletes' state and maximal performance during post-altitude re-acclimatization**

| Period | Changes in the athletes' state and maximal athletic performance | Sources |
|---|---|---|
| $1^{st}$ - $2^{nd}$ days | Favorable state makes it possible to compete and attain good achievements | Fuchs & Reiss, 1990 |
| $3^{rd}$-$7^{th}$ days | Reduced training capacity and low probability of attaining top performance | Schramme, 1970; Pohlitz, 1986 |
| 3rd -$10^{th}$ days | Depressive phase so participation in competition is not recommended | Fuchs & Reiss, 1990 |
| $14^{th}$-$18^{th}$ days | Continual increase in training capacity, and attainment of top performance | Reiss et al., 1969; Suslov & Farfel, 1972 |
| $12^{th}$-$28^{th}$ days | Improvement in general and sport-specific reactions, successful athletic performance | Fuchs & Reiss, 1990; Suslov et al., 1999 |
| $37^{th}$-$46^{th}$ days | Delayed wave of the athletes' improved state, high probability of successful performance | Suslov et al., 1999 |

From the data presented in Table 5.7, three positive phases of post-altitude re-acclimatization can be identified: the first two days after returning to sea level, the period between the $12^{th}$ and $28^{th}$ days, and a more delayed interval between the $37^{th}$ and $46^{th}$ days following altitude camp. The occurrence of the first and second positive phases is supported by many practical observations and is consistent with the findings of several well controlled studies (Figure 5.4).

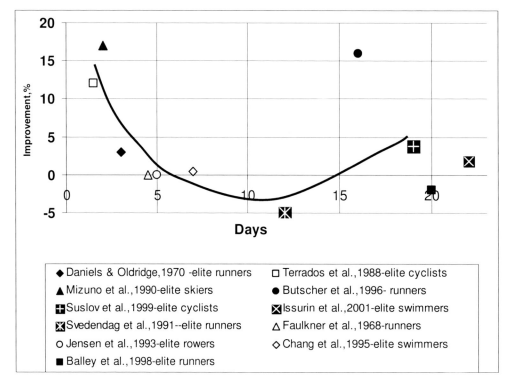

**Figure** 5.**4.** Dependence of performance enhancement on duration of post-altitude acclimatization--summary of studies in different sports

The graph (Figure 5.4.) summarizes the findings recorded after altitude training camps lasting 12-28 days at elevations of 1640-2500m. It shows that positive gains were obtained mostly during the initial two days and 16-20 days after returning to sea level. The majority of impaired performances were recorded between the 5th and 10th days of re-acclimatization. In general, the data reviewed from numerous studies support the existence of two positive phases in the post-altitude period.

Concerning the third delayed phase, its occurrence deserves special attention. There are very few well-documented studies in which the athletes' state and performance were monitored for long periods after altitude training. One such study was carried out during preparation of the USSR national swim team.

**Case study**. Post-altitude performance changes were studied during preparation of the USSR national swim team. The annual plan contained three altitude training camps lasting 20-22 days. During re-acclimatization after the last altitude camp, the swimmers took part in a series of competitions within a 52 day period. The athletes competed in different events and their results were compared to their season best performances and expressed in percentages (Figure 5.5). The best performances were obtained between the 42nd and 47th days and this period was considered as most favorable and recommended for participation in targeted competition (Vaitsekhovsky & Suslov; cited in Suslov et al., 1999).

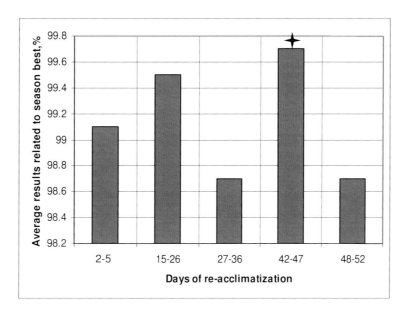

**Figure** 5.5. Performance changes in elite swimmers during re-acclimatization after the third altitude training camp (based on Suslov et al., 1999).
➤ - significant superiority when compared to average results in the first, third, and fifth phases (P<0.05)

In view of the above findings, the post-altitude ergogenic effect can last much longer than previously expected. There is no evidence that hematological, enzymatic and cellular changes induced by altitude training can be maintained for such long periods. However, post-altitude benefits could have contributed to attainment of superior training effects, which led to the delayed best performances. It should be also noted that these impressive performance gains were attained after a series of camps, not from a single training camp. It can therefore be suggested that they are the result of training responses produced by a series of altitude camps. We can also assume that swimmers with unfavorable responses to altitude training were identified in the earlier stages of preparation and did not take part in the final altitude camp. This means that the observed delayed ergogenic effect was achieved by the group of "responders", which could have contributed to the progress attained.

High-performance sport offers many examples of successful preparation exploiting the post-altitude ergogenic effect. Most prominently, endurance athletes of the former GDR attained many outstanding results at the 1988 Seoul Olympic Games using properly timed altitude camps (Table 5.8).

**Table 5.8**

**Timing of altitude training camps of GDR national teams prior the 1988 Seoul Olympic Games (based on Fuchs & Reiss, 1990)**

| Sport | Altitude camp -duration- | Location and elevation | Time to 1st competition -days-* | Time to last competition -days-* |
|---|---|---|---|---|
| Swimming | 23 days | Toluka, 2700 | 20 | 27 |
| Rowing | 23 days* | Kaprun, Silvretta, 1800m | 17 | 23 |
| Road cycling | 18 days | Mexico, 2200m | 41 | 45 |
| Running, middle and long distances | 28-33 days | Mexico, 2200m | 22 | 30 |

* the rowing team had a preliminary 6 days of training in a hypoxic chamber before the altitude camp

In conclusion, it can be said that during the last three decades many athletes and several teams from around the world have exploited the post-altitude ergogenic effect and succeeded at sea-level competitions. Presumably, they belong to the category of "responders" while their coaches belong to the category of "proponents of altitude training". Success in sea-level performance after altitude training programs can be attributed to three general factors:

- selection of athletes who respond positively to altitude training;
- utilization of positive phases of re-acclimatization in planning sea-level performances, and
- designing and creatively implementing a rational training program taking into account the positive and negative phases of re-acclimatization and the individual traits of each athlete

### 5.2.4. Training stage with the altitude camp

There are three different approaches to the design of the training stage containing an altitude camp when preparation is directed toward sea-level performance (Figure 5.6).

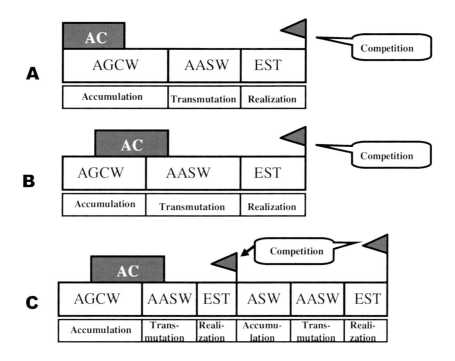

**Figure 5.6.** Three general approaches for designing the training stage containing an altitude camp: A - altitude camp for general conditioning, diversification and active recovery; B - altitude camp for sea-level performance in the second positive phase of re-acclimatization; C - altitude camp for sea-level performance in the third delayed positive phase of re-acclimatization. Key: AC – altitude camp, AGCW – aerobic and general conditioning workloads, AASW – special aerobic-anaerobic workloads, EST – event-specific tapering, ASW – aerobic specific workloads.

Let us consider the above diagram with respect to the particulars of each approach.

Variant A - Altitude camp for general conditioning, diversification and active recovery.

In this case, the training stage can be started with an altitude camp containing non-specific and semi-specific exercises for aerobic and general strength abilities. The following training at sea level is devoted to developing these abilities using sport-specific training means. The next transmutation mesocycle can exploit the positive phase of post-altitude re-acclimatization and the realization mesocycle concludes the training stage.

Variant B - Altitude camp for sea-level performance in the second positive phase of re-acclimatization.

The training stage is started with a pre-altitude training block lasting one-two weeks. It continues with an altitude camp consisting of "soft" aerobic work (acute and transition phases) and "hard" work (stabilization phase). The post-altitude program continues with sport-specific preparation in the transmutation mesocycle, pre-competitive taper and competition.

Variant C - Altitude camp for sea-level performance in the third delayed positive phase (36-46 days after altitude camp). In this case, post-altitude preparation is different. The athletes undergo post-altitude re-acclimatization and take part in competition immediately after the depressive phase (11th-14th days after returning to sea-level) or even a bit earlier. Afterwards, the shortened accumulation and transmutation mesocycles precede the realization mesocycle of optimal duration prior to the targeted-competition.

Interestingly, variant B is the most widely used and discussed in the literature (Reiss & Zansler, 1987; Fuchs & Reiss, 1990), while variant C is less known and less popular. Let us now consider the separate components of variants B and C, namely, pre-altitude and post-altitude preparation.

**Pre-altitude preparation** is intended to improve the athletes' adaptation to hypoxic conditions and the planned aerobic workloads**.** There are two basic approaches, pedagogical and physiological.

The pedagogical approach assumes doing a sea-level block of aerobic workloads (one-three microcycles) focused on extensive use of exercises performed at aerobic and anaerobic threshold levels combined with general conditioning. Two-three days before the altitude camp the workload level is reduced in order to facilitate acute acclimatization during the initial days of altitude camp. This approach is supported by several experts in training athletes (Pfeifer, 1987; Reiss & Zansler, 1987).

The physiological approach employs special techniques to create hypoxic conditions during performance of the exercises at sea-level. This hypoxic training is intended to attain pre-acclimatization before arrival at altitude. Widely used techniques for such training are hypoxic chambers (Wilber, 2004) or special masks for inhaling hypoxic air (Bulgakova et al., 1999). Pre-acclimatization training usually takes one-two weeks and can be completed immediately prior to or a few days before departure (Fuchs & Reiss, 1990). The number of workouts varies from three-six per week with a workout duration of 30-90 min. Various other training regimes have been used although the most widely accepted seems to be continuous and intermittent exercises of moderate intensity.

---

**Example**. German elite walkers Ronald Weigel and Hartwig Gauder, who won two silver and one bronze medal in the Seoul 1988 Olympics practiced at three altitude training camps lasting three-four weeks at elevations of 2400m (Addis Abeba), 2700m (Toluka) and 2000m (Belmeken) with the last one finished 19 days prior to his Olympic performance. Pre-altitude training in a hypoxic chamber lasted one-two weeks prior to each altitude camp (source - Fuchs & Reiss, 1990).

---

**Post-altitude preparation** is based on previously considered phases of sea level re-acclimatization and changes in the athletes' state following altitude training camp (Figure 5.7).

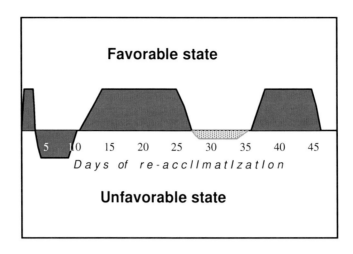

**Figure** 5.**7.** Positive and negative phases of the athletes' state following altitude training, There is insufficient information on the athletes' state between the 28th and 36th days after returning to sea level.

The first positive phase lasting two-three days, has been exploited in athletic performances (sometimes successfully) but still remains problematic in terms of training design. Despite increased work capabilities, this phase includes profound physiological changes caused by drastic changes in environmental conditions. Many experts suggest that this phase should be spent on moderate workloads focused on special conditioning, "soft" predominantly aerobic exercises and technical drills.

**Example**. World-renowned swimming authority Gennady Touretski, who coached a number of world and Olympic winners including the legendary Alexander Popov, notes that the first two days after returning to sea level can be used for competition and be rather successful. However, the high competitive efforts usually aggravate the athletes' state in the subsequent period of re-acclimatization. He is convinced that this early favorable state for athletes should be used to facilitate acute sea-level re-acclimatization. Maximal competitive efforts are not recommended during this phase.

The general approach to training in negative post-altitude phases assumes the use of aerobic and anaerobic threshold level exercises with a gradual increase in the aerobic-anaerobic workloads. This is important during this period to prevent excessive lactate accumulation and to execute sport-specific tasks with increased speed. A compromise between these contradictory demands can be attained with the help of interval series. Alactic bouts at submaximal power can be performed with a focus on "quality", not on movement frequency. Athletes usually do not experience significant problems in techno-tactical drills and attention can be given to accentuated force application in continuous exercises with moderate intensity. After cessation of the negative phase, workouts becomes more economical with medium and moderate intensity (lower heart rate and lactate accumulation) and athletes experience enhanced feelings and better movement control. Highly intense sport-specific exercises can be used without any limitations. As already stated, successful athletic performance can be planned for the period between the 14th and 28th days.

There is very little data on the athletes' state after the second positive post-altitude phase. If the post-altitude training program is focused on a target-competition between days 36-46, the preceding period is devoted to pre-competition preparation. Consequently, the condition of the athlete during this period is determined mostly by current workloads, training residuals of previous work and, to a lesser extent, by the delayed consequences of altitude adaptation. It can be theorized that the benefits of cellular adaptation, such as increased aerobic enzymes, myoglobin, and muscle capillarization, can be maintained for a relatively long period.

There is evidence that additional training in hypoxic chambers is a successful approach during this period (Fuchs & Reiss, 1990). Such altitude-simulated workloads could prolong the previously attained effects including the hypothetical enlargement of the oxygen capacity of blood. In any case, the visible benefit of the third post-altitude positive phase is that it allows more active exploitation of competitive workloads within the Final Stage Preparation for the targeted event.

## 5.2.5. Non-conventional approaches to altitude training and exposure

It has been noted that since the 1968 Mexico City Olympics, the popularity of altitude training has continually increased. Hence, this preparation mode can now be termed conventional. In recent years, modifications of altitude training have appeared and they can be considered non-conventional approaches to athlete preparation (Table 5.9).

**Table 5.9**

**Recent non-conventional approaches to altitude training**

| Approach | Brief description | Sources |
|---|---|---|
| Live High Train Low (LHTL)- natural conditions | Athletes live at altitude and perform their training at (or near) sea level conditions | Levine & Stray-Gundersen, 1997, Chapman et.al., 1998 |
| Live High Train Low (LHTL)- artificial conditions | Athletes live and sleep in simulated altitude environment and perform their training at sea level | Rusko et al., 1995, Nummela & Rusko, 2000 a.o. |
| Training in a hypoxic chamber | Athletes train in artificial conditions of a hypoxic chamber | Terrados et al., 1988, Fuchs & Reiss, 1990 a.o. |

---

**Study and example**. Twenty-two elite male and female runners lived and performed basic continuous training at altitude 2500m for 28 days. Intense interval workloads were performed at altitude 1250m. This design resulted in a high increase in EPO concentration and significant increments of hemoglobin (8%) and erythrocyte mass (4%). After returning to sea level the athletes improved their running performance in 3000m (1%) and maximum oxygen uptake (3%). (Stray-Gundersen et al., 2001).

---

Despite the complexity of this approach it has been applied by several groups of athletes (mostly swimmers and runners), who found it practical, acceptable and promising.

The LHTL approach in artificial conditions assumes use of specially created hypoxic living quarters (room, tent or even apartment), where lower oxygen content is combined with normal barometric pressure (normobaric hypoxia). The greatest expectations from this approach pertain to the hematological factor. For example, living at simulated altitude produces increased synthesis of EPO, hemoglobin and erythrocytes, which cause an increase in maximum oxygen consumption and aerobic performance. These suppositions have been supported in several studies (Mattila & Rusko, 1996; Rusko et al., 1999) but contradict the findings of other researchers (Piel-Aulin et al., 1998; Ashenden et al., 1999, inter alia).

Other promising data relate to the potential benefits of simulated altitude exposure in anaerobic performance. A well-controlled study of high-level male 400m sprinters has shown the significant superiority of ten days of simulated altitude exposure (16-17 hr a day) in comparison to conventional preparation program (Nummela & Rusko, 2000). These outcomes are consistent with the data of trained cyclists, who spent 8-10 hr at a simulated altitude of 2650 m, performed their usual training program and markedly improved their performance and maximal anaerobic ability (Roberts et al., 2003).

---

**Study and example**. Nineteen trained cyclists divided into three groups underwent a preparation program at LHTL and at sea level for 5, 10, and 15 days. They spent 8-10 hr at a simulated altitude 2650 m and performed the usual training program. Performance gains were evaluated in a 4-min maximal cycling trial. The benefit of LHTL mode was confirmed by remarkable gains in Mean Maximal Power Output (4%) and particularly in Maximal Accumulated Oxygen Deficit (10%) compared to the no gains induced by a conventional program. Interestingly, no differences were noted between the changes after 5, 10, and 15 days of training and exposure (Roberts et al., 2003).

---

These data demonstrate the beneficial development of anaerobic ability which is attributed to enhanced muscular buffering capacity. This was confirmed in another study of LHTL at simulated altitude (3000 m) with an exposure duration of 23 days (Gore et al., 2001). At the same time the weaknesses of the artificial LHTL mode should also be considered. One can assume that living in a restricted artificial space may negatively affect the athletes' emotional state, and the hematological benefits still seem dubious. However, even if these benefits are obtained, it is hard to imagine that they can be maintained for two-three weeks until competition.

Training in a hypoxic chamber can be evaluated in two ways: 1) from the outcomes of numerous studies conducted over the last two decades and 2) from practical experiences of supplemental hypoxic training accumulated mostly in Germany.

The first aspect can be illustrated by the findings of several studies that indicated positive training outcomes. The previously described evidence of cellular adaptation was obtained by training one leg in a hypoxic chamber while the second leg was trained at sea level conditions (Terrados et al., 1990). A number of studies were conducted with high-level athletes, who trained for different periods in a hypoxic chamber and didn't register any superior results when compared with the control sea level groups in terms of hematological status and maximum oxygen consumption. However, they did record significant benefits in maximum power output and anaerobic capacity (Terrados et al., 1988; Meeuwsen et al., 2001; Hendriksen & Meeuwsen , 2003).

In contrast to these, a number of other studies were carried out in which simulated altitude training did not elicit positive outcomes in aerobic endurance trials. These well-controlled studies did not reveal any benefits from training in hypoxic conditions, either in long-duration performance or in terms of hematological responses and maximum oxygen consumption (Hahn et al.,1992; Vallier et al., 1996; Karlsen et al., 2002). Apparently, altitude simulated training enables athletes to enhance anaerobic capacity but fails to improve aerobic long-distance endurance.

The second aspect refers to the practical experience of altitude-simulated training approved during the multi-year preparation of elite German athletes (Fuchs & Reiss, 1990; Reiss, 1998). The supplemental training in a hypoxic chamber was incorporated in the annual preparation for various purposes. This included (1) to provide rational pre-altitude preparation (see 5.2.4); (2) to maintain the positive changes induced by a previous altitude training camps and (3) as a rehabilitation program after illness or injury. Correspondingly different training protocols were developed in which the repertory of training means included specific and semi-specific exercises performed running on a treadmill, cycling, rowing and paddling on an ergometer; various simulative exercises and workloads for strength endurance and general conditioning. The integration of altitude-simulated training in the framework of annual preparation is discussed in 5.2.6.

The following summary gives consideration to the potential benefits and particulars of non-conventional approaches to altitude training (Table 5.10).

**Table 5.10**

**Summary of different factors and their expected effects using non-conventional**

**approaches to altitude training**

| Factor | Expected effect | LHTL-natural | LHTL-artificial | Hypoxic chamber training |
|--------|-----------------|--------------|-----------------|--------------------------|
| General ecological influence | Positive emotional impact; favorable response to mountain conditions, clean fresh air, lack of urban stressors, etc. | yes | no | no |
| Increased exercise intensity | Earlier development of aerobic-anaerobic and anaerobic abilities | yes | yes | yes |
| Hematological changes | Increased hemoglobin, erythrocyte mass and oxygen capacity of the blood | yes | ??? | no |
| Cellular adaptation | Increased aerobic enzymes, myoglobin and muscle capillarization | no | no | yes |
| Anaerobic capacity | Enhanced anaerobic performance due to the increased buffering capacity of the muscles | yes | yes | yes |

The general ecological influence of altitude exposure refers to its' influence on the emotional and neuro-physiological spheres that is multilateral and, as a rule, highly positive. The exciting and magnificent beauty of mountains, clean, fresh, cool air, lack of typical urban stressors like noise, transportation pollution, endless bustle etc. all positively affect recovery and behavior as a whole. All these benefits increase the effectiveness of LHTL under natural conditions. In contrast, LHTL under artificial conditions has the obvious disadvantage of prolonged exposure to a closed-in and limited living space.

All of the non-conventional approaches considered have visible benefits when compared to traditional altitude camps with regard to unlimited (or less limited) employment of intense exercises. Indeed, this is one of the important reasons why these approaches and techniques were developed.

The hematological factor seems to be relevant in each of the approaches. In fact, its effect in LHTL in artificial conditions was not supported by the outcomes of several studies, and wasn't found with regard to training in a hypoxic chamber. The latter has promising benefits for muscular cellular adaptation, which can hardly be expected following training in normo-baric conditions (LHTL modes). A stimulating effect on anaerobic capacity can be expected after each of the above non-conventional approaches.

## 5.2.6. Altitude training as a part of the annual preparation cycle

If attitude training is incorporated in a preparation program its placement in the annual plan is very important. Following the first general principle of altitude training (5.2.1), planning is very different for altitude and for sea level performances. The annual preparation plan for a targeted competition at altitude is characterized by a longer total duration of altitude exposure, relatively more prolonged altitude camps and scheduling the last altitude camp to immediately precede the target competition (Figure 5.8).

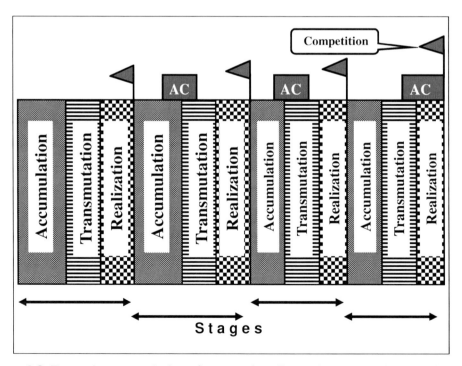

**Figure 5.8.** Exemplary annual plan of preparation directed to targeted competitions at altitude (based on Issurin & Vrijens, 1995): AC – altitude camp

It is worth noting that altitude camps encompass a part of the accumulation mesocycle when the training program is extensive and does not exceed the anaerobic threshold level. The second part of altitude exposure can include intense and even severe exercises and belongs to the transmutation mesocycle.

Annual plans directed to target-competition at sea level can be structured with two different designs: (a) when the Final Stage Preparation (FSP) is relatively short and exploits the second positive phase of re-acclimatization after the last altitude camp, (b) when the FSP is more prolonged and exploits the more delayed consequences of the altitude training (Figure 5.9).

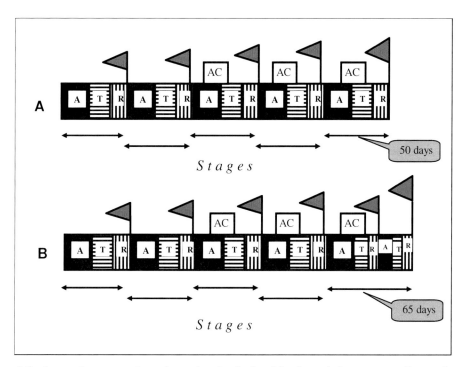

**Figure** 5.9. Annual preparation plans that include altitude training camps directed to the targeted competition at sea level: A – FSP exploits the second positive phase of post-altitude re-acclimatization; B - FSP exploits the third positive phase of post-altitude re-acclimatization.

Plan A is more popular and was widely used in the preparation of world-leading athletes from the former GDR (Pfeifer, 1987; Fuchs & Reiss, 1990) and the USSR (Suslov, 1983; Kaverin & Issurin, 1990). Plan B is less known and is not discussed in the available literature although it was successfully used many times in the preparation of top-level athletes as for example, GDR road cyclists, USSR canoe-kayak paddlers, and others. The benefits of plan B are mostly in methodology, the use of highly intense workloads in a favorable re-acclimatization phase and participation in prior competition raises self-confidence levels and facilitates techno-tactical innovations. However, there is no evidence that potential physiological post-altitude benefits can be prolonged for a period of 36-45 days.

For a long time, training experts have strived to rationalize annual preparation so that it combines traditional and non-conventional altitude training approaches. An example of such a creative approach is the annual preparation of German 50 km walkers, who won silver and bronze medals in the 1988 Seoul Olympics (Figure 5.10).

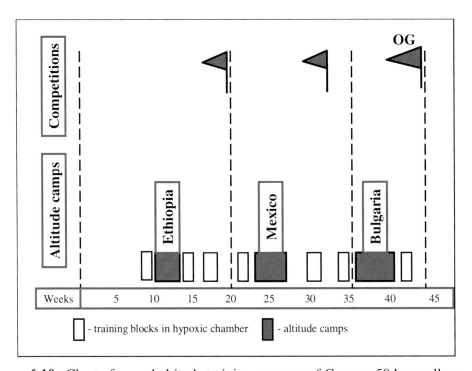

**Figure 5.10.** Chart of annual altitude training program of German 50 km walkers before the 1988 Seoul Olympic Games (based on Fuchs & Reiss, 1990)

The above diagram illustrates the annual training program in which each of three altitude camps was combined with altitude-simulated training blocks in pre- and post-altitude periods. It was hypothesized that such a combination makes it possible to:

(a) facilitate acute adaptation at the beginning of each altitude camp because the athletes experience a pre-acclimatization program in a hypoxic chamber;

(b) prolong the ergogenic altitude effect of the preceding camp using altitude-simulated workloads and;

(c) diversify the sea level training program and attain higher training responses.

Interestingly, these successful German walkers took part in Olympic competition 19 days after the last altitude camp and this post-altitude program contained a thoroughly designed altitude-simulated training block. It is believed that further progress in altitude programs will include rational sequencing and a combination of traditional and non-conventional approaches to altitude preparation.

**5.2.7 Guidelines for structuring an altitude preparation program**

Despite the specificity and properties of different sports, general guidelines for structuring a preparation program containing altitude training can be established (Table 5.11). These guidelines refer to general principles (5.2.1), phases of altitude acclimatization (5.2.2), post-altitude re-acclimatization (5.2.3), characteristics of several training stages containing an altitude camp (5.2.4) and design for the entire annual cycle (5.2.6).

The guidelines do not address non-conventional approaches to altitude training that are still not widely used. It is obvious that they can enrich the traditional repertory but it should be kept in mind that utilizing them demands sophisticated conditions and extensive knowledge.

**Table 5.11**

**General guidelines for structuring a preparation program containing altitude training camps**

| Objectives | Comments |
|---|---|
| Developing proper concepts of athletes' preparation containing altitude training | The general purpose, number, duration, timing and location of altitude camps should be reasonably determined |
| Selecting appropriate athletes for participation in the altitude program | The individual reactivity of athletes with respect to "responders" and "non-responders" should be taken into consideration |
| Determining a general approach to planning the training stages containing an altitude camp | The training stage chart should be designed with respect to pre-altitude and post-altitude preparation phases |
| Selecting and facilitating appropriate means to monitor training responses at altitude | Ordering blood analyses, body weight measurements, HR monitors and blood lactate analyzers require special attention |
| Structuring a training program for pre-altitude, altitude proper and post-altitude preparation phases | The training program should take into consideration individual training responses including phases of acclimatization and re-acclimatization |
| Providing special care regarding nutrition and use of dietary supplements | Water balance, possible iron deficit and muscular catabolic responses should be given particular attention |
| Planning post-altitude trials and competitions | The sport-specific trials and competitive program should reflect the favorable states of post-altitude re-acclimatization |
| Implementing the program of pre-altitude, altitude proper and post-altitude programs in each specific training stage | Individual training responses are monitored and used for ongoing modifications in preparation |
| Retrospective analysis of training responses at altitude and post-altitude effects following the entire annual cycle | Overall conclusions and recommendations for further preparation are required |

**Summary**

The initial impetus to study altitude training and performance was fueled by the need to compete in high prestige events like the 1960 Winter Olympics and the 1968 Summer Olympics. The further development of altitude training has been oriented mostly towards preparation for sea level performances. A review of the current literature allows us to reconstruct the physiological changes that take place during altitude acclimatization. Most notable is that the human responses in the acute phase differ widely from those seen during more delayed periods of adaptation (Table 5.2).

The current grasp of altitude training is contradictory. Many exercise physiology textbooks declare that altitude training provides no benefits for sea level performances when compared to proper conventional training, while coaching publications consider altitude training as an efficacious and practice-proven tool to enhance high-performance preparation. This contradiction can be partly explained by the variety of individual training responses to altitude training, i.e., the individual predisposition of some athletes being more favorable. Nevertheless, the potential benefits of altitude training for enhancement of sea level performance include the following: (1) improved oxygen delivery to muscles induced by higher oxygen-carrying capacity of blood, (2) enhanced oxygen utilization within the muscle cells due to the greater activity of aerobic enzymes and increased myoglobin content and (3) increased anaerobic capacity via improved buffering capacity in muscles and blood.

The general principles of altitude training are based on the importance of several primary goals of preparing athletes for altitude or sea-level performance, or using the altitude camp for active recovery and diversification. It is also based on the selection of athletes who respond positively to altitude training, the structure of the altitude training program in accordance with phases of acclimatization, and the design of the post-altitude training program based on phases of sea level re-acclimatization.

Acclimatization at altitude is divided into three phases. The first one – acute acclimatization – is restricted mostly to training capacity and its duration (3-7 days) strongly depends on each athlete's individual peculiarities. The second transition phase brings more favorable but unstable and less predictable responses. Its duration also varies according to the individual and lasts 3-5 days. The third stabilization phase allows athletes to perform a training program with large workloads almost without limitation. The general approach is to construct a training program according to the phases of acclimatization (Table 5.6). Similarly, post-altitude preparation is affected by phases of sea-level re-acclimatization and this determines the favorable periods for competition, mainly, the intervals between days 14-28, and between days 36–46.

Special attention is given to structuring a training cycle containing an altitude camp. Usually the first part of an altitude program consists of medium intensity aerobic exercises that correspond to the content of the accumulation mesocycle. The second part of the altitude camp can include highly intense aerobic-anaerobic and anaerobic exercises which are typical of the transmutation mesocycle. High performances can be planned between days 14-28, and between days 36–46. Correspondingly, the training stage can be shorter or longer. When the training is intended to exploit the post-altitude ergogenic effect, the annual cycle includes two-three training stages with an altitude camp.

In addition to traditional altitude training, where athletes live and train at the same elevation, several non-conventional approaches have appeared: (1) athletes live at altitude but train lower; (2) athletes live at altitude-simulated conditions and train at sea level; (3) athletes live at sea-level and train in altitude-simulated conditions. All of these techniques have their advantages and disadvantages (Table 5.10) and can be creatively implemented in the preparation of an athlete.

## References for Chapter 5

Ashenden, M.J., Gore, C.J., Dobson, G.P. et al.(1999). "Live high, train low" does not change the total hemoglobin mass of male endurance athletes sleeping at a simulated altitude of 3000-m for 23 nights. *Eur J Appl Physiol*, 80:479-484.

Balley, D.M., Davies, B., Romer,L. et al. (1998). Implications of moderate altitude training for sea-level endurance in elite distance runners. *Eur J Appl Physiol*, 78:360-368.

Boning, D. (1997). Altitude and hypoxic training – a short review. *Int J Sport Med*, 18:565-570.

Brooks, G.A., Fahey, T.D., White, T.P. (1996). *Exercise physiology. Human bioenergetics and its applications.* London: Mayfield Publisher.

Butscher, M., Nachbauer, W., Baumgartl, P. et al. (1996). Benefits of training at moderate altitude versus sea level training in amateur runners. *Eur J Appl Physiol,*, 74:558-563.

Chung, D.-S., Lee, J.-G., Kim, E.-H. et al. (1995). The effects of altitude training on blood cells, maxmal oxygen uptake and swimming performance. *Korean Journal of Science*, 7:35-46.

Chapman, R.E., Stray-Gundersen,J., Levine, B.D. (1998). Individual variations in response to altitude training. *Journ Appl Phys.*, 85:1448-1456.

Daniels, J., Oldridge, N.(1970). The effects of alternate exposure to altitude and sea level in world-class middle distance runners. *Med Sci Sports*, 2:107-112.

Ekblom, B.,Berglund, B. (1991). Effect of erythropoietin administration on maximal aerobic power. Scand. *Journ. Med. Sc. Sports*, 1: 88-93.

Faulkner, J.A., Kollias, J., Favour, C.B. et al. (1968). Maximum aerobic capacity and running performance at altitude. *J Appl Physiol*, 24:685-691.

Frederick, E.C. (1974). Training at altitude. In: *The complete runner.* Mountain View, CA: World Publications, 38-52.

Fuchs U., Reiss M. (1990). *Hohentraining. Das Erfolgkonzept der Ausdauersportarten.* Munster: Philippka.

deGaray,A.,Levine,L., and Carter, J.E.L. (1974). *Genetic and anthropomrtric syudies of Olympic Athletes.* New York.: Academic Press.

Gore, C.J., Hahn, A.G., Aughey, D.et al. (2001). Live high:train low increases muscle buffer capacity and submaximal cycling efficiency. *Acta Phys Scand*, 173:275-286.

Hahn, A.G., Telford, R.D., Timilty, M.E. et al. (1992). Effect of supplemental hypoxic training on physiological characteristics and ergometer performance of elite rowers. Excel, 8:127-138.

Hendriksen I.J., Meeuwsen, T. (2003). The effect of intermittent training in hypobaric hypoxia on sea-level exercises: A cross-over study in humans. *Eur J Appl Physiol,*, 88:396-403.

Issurin V., Kaverin V. (1990). *Specialized preparation of canoe-kayak paddlers. Recommendations for coaching.* Moscow: State Committee USSR for Physical Culture and Sport.

Issurin V.,Vrijens, J.(1996). Altitude training in elite sport. *Flamish Journal for Sports Medicine and Sport Science.* 7,66,24-41.

Issurin, V., Shkliar, V., Kaufman, L.( 2001). Concept of the modern training in medium height mountains: ergogenic effect and methodical principles of training. *Sport Science.* Vilnius, 4(26), 4-18.

Jensen, C., Fisher, A. (1979). *Scientific basis of athletic conditioning.* Philadelphia: Lea & Febiger.

Jensen, K., Nielsen, T., Fiskenstrand, A. et al. (1993). High-altitude training does not increase maximal oxygen uptake or work capacity at sea level in rowers. *Scand J Med Sci Sports*, 3; 256-262.

Karlsen,T., Madsen, O., Rolf, S. and Stray-Gundersen,J.(2002). Effects of 3 weeks hypoxic interval training on sea level cycling performance and hematological parameters. *Med Sci Sports Exerc*, 34 (Suppl.5):S224.

Levine, B.D., Stray-Gundersen,J. (1997). "Living high-training low": Effect of moderate altitude acclimatization with low altitude training on performance. *J Appl Physiol*, 83:102-112.

Mattila, V., Rusko, H. (1996). Effect of living high and training low on sea level performance in cyclists. *Med Sci Sports Exer*, 28 (Suppl.5):S517.

McArdle,W.D., Katch,F., Katch,V. (1991). *Exercise physiology.* Philadelphia/ London: Lea & Febiger

Meeuwsen, T., Hendriksen, I.J., Holewijn, M.(2001). Training induced increases in sea-level performances are enhanced by acute intermittent hypobaric hypoxia. *Eur J Appl Physiol*, 84:283-290.

Mizuno, M.C., Juel,T., Bro-Rasmussen E. et al. (1990). Limb skeletal muscle adaptations in athletes after training at altitude. *J Appl Physiol*, 68:496-502.

Nummela, A., Rusko,H. (2000). Acclimatization to altitude and normoxic training improve 400-m running performance at sea level. *J Sport Sci*, 18:411-419.

Piel-Aulin, K., Svedenhag,L., Wide,B. et al. (1998). Short-term intermittent normobaric hypoxia – hematological, physiological and mental effects. *Scand J Med Sci Sports*, 8: 132-137.

Pfeifer, H. (1987). Zyklisierung und Akzentuierung von Belastungssteigerungen und hoher Leistungsfahigkeit fur geplannte Zeitpunkt im Sportschwimmen. *Theorie und Praxis Leistungssport*. Berlin 25, 3:49-61.

Pohlitz,L.(1986 ). Praktische Einfahrungen im Hohentraining mit Mittelstrecklerinnen. *Leistungssport*, 2, 23-26.

Reiss,M., Fuchs, U., Pfefferkorn, B. et al. (1969). Hohentraining und Nachhoheneffect Untersuchungen uber ihren Einfluss auf die Dynamics des Trainingszustanden und dir sportliche Form im Mittelstreckenlauf. *Theorie und Praxis Leistungssport*, 9, 87-123.

Reiss, M., Zansler,H. (1987). Anzatze fur Erhohung der Leistungswirksamkeit der Trainingkonzeption in den Ausdauersportarten. *Theorie und Praxis Leistungssport*. Berlin 25, 2:26-51.

Reiss, M. (1998). Hauptrichtungen des Einzatzes und der Methodik des Hohentraining in den Ausdauersportarten. *Lestungssport*, 4:21-28.

Rusko, H., Leppavuori, A., Makela, P. et al.(1995). Living high, training low: A new approach to altitude training at sea level in athletes. *Med Sci Sports Exerc*, 27 (Suppl.5):S6..

Roberts, A.D., Clark, S.A., Townsend, N.E. et al.(2003). Changes in performance, maximal oxygen uptake maximal accumulated oxygen deficit after 5, 10 and 15 days of live high: train low altitude exposure. *Eur J Appl Physiol*, 88:390-395.

Saltin,B. (1996). Adaptive responses to training at medium altitude; with a note on Kenyan runners and a proposal for a multi-centre study. *Research Quarterly*, 67: 1-10.

Schramme R. (1970). Die Nutzung des Hohentrainings zur Leistungssteigerungen bei Wettkamfen unter NN-bedinggungen in Schwimmen. *Theorie und Praxis Leistungssport*. Berlin, 4, 84-87.

Stray-Gundersen,J., Chapman, R.T., Levine, B.D. (2001). "Living high-training low" altitude training improves sea level performance in male and female elite runners. *J Appl Physiol*, 91:1113-1120.

Svedenhag, J., Saltin,B., Johansson, C. et al.(1991). Anaerobic and aeroboc exercise capacities of elite middle-distance runners after two weeks training at moderate altitude. *Scand. J Med Sci Sports*, 1: 205-214.

Suslov,F. (1983). *Altitude training as the method to improve athletic mastership.* Thesis of Doctor of Sciences dissertation. Moscow: Pedagogical University.

Suslov, F., Farfel,V. (1972 ). Performances and training capacity during re-acclimatization after altitude training. *Theor.Pract.Phys.Cult.*, 11, 38-39.

Suslov, F., Gippenreuter E., Kholodov, Zh. (1999). *Sport training at altitude conditions.* Moscow: FGAPK..

Telford, R.D., Graham, K.S., Sutton, J.R. et al.(1996). Medium altitude training and sea-level performance. *Med Sci Sports Exerc.*, 28(Suppl.5):S124.

Terrados, N., Melichna,C.,Sylven,E. et al.(1988). Effects of training at simulated altitude on performance and muscle metabolic capacity in competitive road cyclists. *Eur J Appl Physiol*, 57:203-209.

Terrados, N., Jansson, E., Sylven, C. et al. (1990). Is hypoxia a stimulus for synthesis of oxydative enzymes and myoglobin ? *J Appl Physiol*, 68:2369-2372.

Vallier, J.M., Chateau, P., Guezennec, C.Y. (1996). Effect of high-intensity training in a hypobaric chamber on the physical performance of competitive triathletes. *Eur Appl Physiol*, 73:471-478.

Vogt, M.A., Puntschart,J., Geiser,C. et al. (2001). Molecular adaptation in human skeletal muscle to endurance training under simulated hypoxic conditions. *J Appl Physiol*, 91:173-182.

Wilber, R.L. (2004). *Altitude training and athletic performance.* Champaign, IL: Human Kinetics.

Wilmore, J., Costill, D. (1993). *Training for sport and activity. Physiological basis of the conditioning process.* Champaign, IL: Human Kinetics.

Witkovski,S., Chen, J., Stray-Gundersen, R.L. et al.(2002). Genetic markers for erithropojetic responses to altitude. *Med Sci Sports Exerc*, 34(Suppl.5):S246.

# Glossary

*aerobic endurance (capacity)* – Ability to sustain fatigue in exercises where energy is
   supplied with the use of oxygen

*anaerobic glycolitic endurance (capacity)* - Ability to sustain fatigue in exercises
   where energy is predominantly supplied with anaerobic glycolitic reactions

*anaerobic threshold* - The level of effort where lactate levels begin to rise.

*blood Lactate* - Physiological indicator of glycolisis activation or anaerobic
metabolism.

*blood urea* - Physiological indicator of metabolic fatigue and metabolic recovery.

*catecholamines (adrenaline and noradrenaline)* – Hormones produced by the
   adrenal medulla for rapid activation of metabolic reactions during excitation,
   physical effort and emotional tension.

*cardiac output* - The volume of blood pumped by the heart in liters/minute.

*conjugated effect exercises* -  Exercises that combine motor ability and technical
   skill.

*cortisol* – Hormone that controls metabolism of carbohydrates and fats, acts as an
   anti-inflammatory agent and stimulates breakdown of protein.

*creatine phosphokinase (CPK)* - Blood enzyme that reflects the level of muscle tissue
   breakdown and serves as an indicator of protein metabolism

*creatinphosphate* – An energy-rich substance that plays a crucial role for providing
   energy in short-term highly intense exercises.

*detraining* – Decrease in functional capabilities of an athlete due to insufficient
   training stimuli.

*erythropoietin (EPO)* - A hormone, produced by the kidney, which stimulates the
   bone marrow to produce red blood cells.

*fartlek* -  The term that is usually used for describing a wide spectrum of non-uniform
   continuous exercises

*glycogen* – The carbohydrate storage located in muscles and liver.

*hypoxia* – A reduced availability of oxygen to the tissues.

*key-exercise (or key-task)* - The main element (drill, fight or match) in a single
   workout.

*key-workout* - The most important developmental workout which is focused on the
   main training objective.

***maximal anaerobic glycolitic power*** – Maximum amount of work per minute attained in exercises where the energy is supplied predominantly by anaerobic glycolitic reactions.

***maximum oxygen consumption (maximal aerobic power)*** - The maximum amount of oxygen that an individual can utilize in a defined period of time.

***mesocycle-blocks:***

*accumulation mesocycle* – Employed to develop basic motor and technical abilities and to increase the motor potential of the athlete.

*transmutation mesocycle* – Employed to transfer the increased generalized motor abilities into event-specific athletic preparedness.

*realization mesocycle* – Used for attainment of full restoration and event-specific readiness for the forthcoming trial or competition.

***microcycles:***

*adjustment* – Devoted to initial adaptation to appropriate workloads.

*loading* – Devoted to fitness development. It is the most widely used type of microcycle.

*impact* – Microcycle using extreme training stimuli.

*pre-competitive* – Devoted to immediate preparation for forthcoming competition.

*competitive* – Microcycle where the athlete takes part in competition.

*restoration* – Used for active recovery of the athlete.

***muscle buffering capacity*** – The ability of muscles to tolerate the acid that accumulates in them during anaerobic workloads.

***overload principle*** - Postulates that a fitness gain requires a load (stimulus) that exceeds the accustomed to level.

***responders (high, medium, and low)*** – The athletes who manifest a high, medium, or low response to training stimuli.

***sensitive periods*** - The periods in long-term preparation of the young athlete when he/she is more trainable in certain motor abilities than at other times.

***somatotype*** - Characteristics of the body that include linear, circular and fat measurements in human body.

***sport giftedness*** - Predisposition to and higher trainability to a certain athletic activity. They are referred to as genetically transmitted properties of the individual.

***sport talent*** – Optimal combination of psycho-physiological, anthropometric and mental properties of the individual that allow him/her to attain sport excellence.

***stretch-shortening cycle*** – Muscle action consisting of eccentric (stretch) and concentric (shortening) phases.

***supercompensation cycle*** – Sequence of physiological reactions from a single or series of workloads to attain a higher than pre-load level of fitness.

***targeted ability*** – The ability (physical or technical) upon which the training workload has an effect.

***testosterone*** – The predominant male sex hormone.

***trainability*** – The athletes' ability to react positively to training stimuli

***training cycles***:

*microcycle* – Small training cycle containing a number of training days.

*mesoocycle* – Medium size training cycle containing a number of microcycles.

*macrocycle* – Big training cycle containing a number of mesocyces.

*annual cycle* - Big training cycle containing the preparation for one year.

*quadrennial (Olympic) cycle* – Training cycle comprised of four annual cycles.

***training effects*** – Changes in the athlete's state induced by training.

*acute effect* - Changes in body state that occur during the exercise.

*immediate effect* – Changes in body state resulting from a single workout or/and single training day.

*cumulative effect* - Changes in body state and level of motor/technical abilities resulting from a series of workouts.

*delayed effect* - Changes in body state and level of motor/technical abilities attained over a given time interval after a specific training program.

*residual effect* - Retention of changes in body state and motor abilities after the cessation of training beyond a given time period.

***training means*** - Refers to all modalities involved in the program.

***training block*** - A training cycle of highly concentrated specialized workloads.

***training periodization*** - The purposeful sequencing of different training units and cycles so that the athlete can attain the desired state and planned for results.

# About the Author

 **Prof., Dr. Vladimir B. Issurin** serves as a scientific and professional coordinator of the Elite Sport Department of the Israeli Olympic Committee at the Wingate Institute. He completed his undergraduate studies in Sport Sciences and his Ph.D. dissertation on aquatic motor fitness and movement technique of swimmers in the Leningrad Sport University (1963-1972). His post-doctoral studies on motor/ technical sportsmanship in individual water sports were completed at Moscow Sport University (1988). He served as a scientific adviser and head of the scientific group for the USSR Olympic canoe/kayak team during three quadrennial cycles (1978-1991) and earned two government awards.

Since 1991, professor Issurin has lived in Israel and works as a researcher in the Sports Science Department (1991-94), is a professional consultant and coordinator of the Israeli Olympic National teams (since 1992), and lecturer at the Wingate coaching school and Wingate Physical Education College. He was advisor of 21 Ph.D. dissertations in the theory, physiology and biomechanical branches of sports training. As a member of the national Olympic delegations he took part in five Olympic Games; twice as a team leader of Israeli kayak and swimming national teams (2000 and 2004). He has over 150 scientific articles in national and international journals and in edited books and given over 50 international presentations.

He has lectured at universities and coaching forums in Athens, Bangkok, Florence, Ghent, Gijon, Göteborg, Grand Rapids (Michigan), Jyvaskyla, Kiev, Köln, Leuven, Lisbon, Madrid, Magdeburg, Moscow, Palma de Mallorca, Pontevedra, Poznan, Prague, Riga, Rome, St.Petersburg, Sofia, Tashkent, Tallinn, Vilnius and Volgograd. He has authored or coauthored 9 books. He has received honorary awards of the Olympic Committees of USSR, Bulgaria and Lithuania. Dr. Issurin is a member of the International Informatization Academy associated with UNESCO. He is an Editorial Board member of the *Journal of Sports Medicine and Physical Fitness* and reviewer for the scientific journals, *Sports Medicine* and *European Journal of Sport Sciences*. Currently his research is focused on the methodology of high-performance training and further development of the original coaching concepts for elite athletes. He is a multi-champion of Israel in masters swimming competitions.

# COMING SOON

# Principles and basics of advanced training of athletes

## By Vladimir Issurin, Ph.D.

The purpose of this second book by Dr. Issurin to be published by Ultimate Athlete Concepts is to provide basic knowledge on general training backgrounds, to summarize up-to-date information on basic concepts of training effects and athletes' trainability, and to share new knowledge on training design and evaluation in view of the non-traditional periodization concept.

The book contains materials and findings, which taken as a whole, fulfill the purpose of this book. The basic terms, methods and principles of sports training, which clarify the comprehensive mechanisms of physical fitness improvement, are presented with up-to-date interpretations. The sport-specific principles of adaptation and general principles of athletic training are presented in light of contemporary views of athletic training. The effects produced by systematic training are the particular focus of the author. An unequivocal understanding of training effects requires special elucidation which the author intends to provide. Indeed, practical needs dictate making a distinction between short-term and long-term responses in athletes. Such relatively new concepts as delayed and residual training effects have great importance both as scientific background and for the design of practical training programs.

Likewise, athlete trainability, meaning the ability to respond positively to training workloads, takes on paramount importance in sport science and athletic training. Everyone knows that trainability is a decisive factor in sport progress, but questions remain. This includes how does this factor work? What constitutes the limit of trainability? What form does trainability take with regard to different human skills and capabilities? All these aspects are thoroughly considered with regard to practical needs of coaches and athletes.

A substantial part of the book is devoted to designing the training programs. The author's descriptions touch on traditional training periodization, which was promulgated more than five decades ago, and non-traditional approaches to periodization, which continue to draw the interest of coaches, athletes, and training analysts. This interest is partly satisfied by the first book of this series, "Block Periodization: Breakthrough in Sports Training". In this second book, inquisitive readers will find unfamiliar thoughts and concepts about Block Periodization training.

More specifically, aspects of peaking that are extremely important for competitive sport are considered in light of Block Periodization and the successful experiences of top-level athletes. The modeling approaches, which are presented in the last chapter of the book, can be very productive in terms of concretizing training targets, individual and collective norms of sport-specific abilities and training workloads. All parts of the book contain unique findings of author, which been collected during his long-term practical work with East European (mostly Soviet) and Western coaches and athletes.

# ALSO AVAILABLE

# from Ultimate Athlete Concepts

## Build a Better Athlete
### by Dr. Michael Yessis

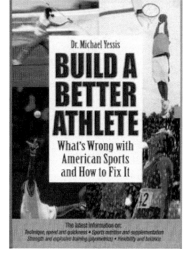

This book by Dr. Yessis is the **most comprehensive sports training book ever written** on what it takes to develop an athlete. It covers technique of the basic skills, the physical qualities needed for sports in general, for specific sports, and how they should be developed. In addition, specific recommendations on nutrition –that have never before been presented to athletes—are given in easy to understand terms. There is also a chapter on the role of vision and vision training.

The book is a culmination of over 50 years of working with and teaching athletes how to develop their full potential and be successful in their chosen sport. It is unmatched in not only it's scope, but in the detail given to each of the factors. Many of the concepts presented are **state-of-the-art and have been proven** in practice. In fact, the information is based not only on the knowledge available in the U.S. but in the leading sporting nations.

This book is of great benefit to coaches, athletes and parents who are working with their youngsters to improve performance. Especially valuable are the chapters dealing with the basic skills of throwing, jumping, hitting, running and kicking. By learning what constitutes effective technique and how it can be taught and/or improved the athletes often improve more than if they only did conditioning work, playing and practicing.

## Explosive Running
### by Michael Yessis, Ph.D.

**This book is a book of firsts not seen in any other running book!** If you have ever wanted to improve your running, there has never been a better time to start. Explosive Running is the answer to your running woes. Not only does this book explain the mechanics of running, but it breaks down running technique into easy to follow steps. No other book comes close to matching the specificity of the running technique analyses and the specialized strength and explosive exercises presented in this book. Also covered are Active stretches, barefoot running, how to fix common problems, nutrition specific to running and how to set up and conduct the workout program. Serious sprinters, long distance and running athletes in other sports should not be without it.

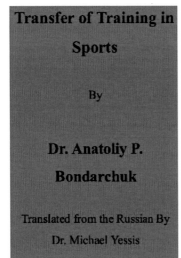

**Transfer of Training in Sports**

**By**

**Dr. Anatoliy P. Bondarchuk**

Translated from the Russian By Dr. Michael Yessis

# Transfer of Training in Sport

## by Anatoly Bondarchuk

Translated by Dr. Michael Yessis

Transfer of Training is the first definitive book on what transfer of training is and what is involved to truly enhance performance with the use of specific exercises. Based on 10 years of study of the highest level athletes, Dr. Bondarchuk brings out which commonly used "specific" exercises truly enhance performance in throwing, jumping and running, and general principles such as conjugated effects.

Great detail is given to the transfer of physical qualities when using different types of exercises in the sprints, throws and jumps as well as in cyclical events that require endurance. Equal attention is given to the transfer of motor skills including the learning and improvement of technique and the influence of different intensity exercises.

This book has changed the way many athletes train to improve their performance. It is a must for all creative coaches.

# SPORTS: Is it all B.S.?
## By Dr. Michael Yessis

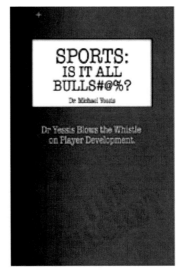

This book is a great read for everyone interested in sports and a must read for anyone who has an athlete in the family, especially if the athlete would like to develop his or her full potential. The information appeals to not only people who are interested in sports, but to the nation as a whole. It has ramifications regarding our participation in World and Olympic Games.

In a nation that has more money spent on sports, more coaches, more and better equipment and facilities and more athletes than any other nation, collegiate and professional teams must go to foreign countries to get the best players. This is a deplorable state of affairs. Even a small country such as Greece can beat our best professional basketball players. Ask yourself why Cuba can beat our best professional baseball players, our most popular national game.

*Sports: Is It All B.S.?*, is an expose of the many myths and false information that have surrounded sports in the U.S. for many decades. One reason for the sheer amount of misinformation is that we, as a nation, do not have a scientifically-based training system, nor do we have universities or schools that specialize in development of coaches and athletes. This is why we have to travel the world over to find the best athletes for our collegiate and professional teams.